Rocks and Minerals

TEACHER'S GUIDE

SCIENCE AND TECHNOLOGY FOR CHILDREN®

NATIONAL SCIENCE RESOURCES CENTER
Smithsonian Institution • National Academy of Sciences
Arts and Industries Building, Room 1201
Washington, DC 20560

NSRC

The National Science Resources Center is operated by the Smithsonian Institution and the National Academy of Sciences to improve the teaching of science in the nation's schools. The NSRC collects and disseminates information about exemplary teaching resources, develops and disseminates curriculum materials, and sponsors outreach activities, specifically in the areas of leadership development and technical assistance, to help school districts develop and sustain hands-on science programs.

STC Project Supporters

National Science Foundation
Smithsonian Institution
U.S. Department of Defense
U.S. Department of Education
John D. and Catherine T. MacArthur Foundation
The Dow Chemical Company Foundation
E. I. du Pont de Nemours & Company
Amoco Foundation, Inc.
Hewlett-Packard Company
Smithsonian Institution Educational Outreach Fund
Smithsonian Women's Committee

This project was supported, in part,
by the
National Science Foundation
Opinions expressed are those of the authors
and not necessarily those of the Foundation

ISBN 0-89278-970-0

Published by Carolina Biological Supply Company, 2700 York Road, Burlington, NC 27215.
Call toll free 1-800-334-5551.

This material is based upon work supported by the National Science Foundation under Grant No. ESI-9252947. Any opinions, findings, and conclusions or recommendations expressed in this material are those of the author(s) and do not necessarily reflect the views of the National Science Foundation.

CB787370109

♻ Printed on recycled paper.

Foreword

Since 1988, the National Science Resources Center (NSRC) has been developing Science and Technology for Children® (STC®), an innovative hands-on science program for children in grades kindergarten through six. The 24 units of the STC program, four for each grade level, are designed to provide all students with stimulating experiences in the life, earth, and physical sciences and technology while simultaneously developing their critical-thinking and problem-solving skills.

The STC units provide children with the opportunity to learn age-appropriate concepts and skills and to acquire scientific attitudes and habits of mind. In the primary grades, children begin their study of science by observing, measuring, and identifying properties. Then they move on through a progression of experiences that culminate in grade six with the design of controlled experiments.

The "Focus-Explore-Reflect-Apply" learning cycle incorporated into the STC units is based on

Alignment of STC® and STC/MS™ Science Curriculum Modules

Grade Level		Life and Earth Sciences		Physical Science and Technology	
STC	K–1	Organisms	Weather	Solids and Liquids	Comparing and Measuring
	2	The Life Cycle of Butterflies	Soils	Changes	Balancing and Weighing
	3	Plant Growth and Development	Rocks and Minerals	Chemical Tests	Sound
	4	Animal Studies	Land and Water	Electric Circuits	Motion and Design
	5	Microworlds	Ecosystems	Food Chemistry	Floating and Sinking
	6	Experiments with Plants	Measuring Time	Magnets and Motors	The Technology of Paper
STC/MS	6–8	Human Body Systems	Catastrophic Events	Properties of Matter	Energy, Machines, and Motion
	6–8	Organisms—From Macro to Micro	Earth in Space	Light	Electrical Energy and Circuit Design

Note: All STC units can be used at one grade level above or below the level indicated on the chart. STC/MS units can also be used at grade 9.

Sequence of Development of Scientific Reasoning Skills

Scientific Reasoning Skills	Grades					
	1	2	3	4	5	6
Observing, Measuring, and Identifying Properties	♦	♦	♦	♦	♦	♦
Seeking Evidence Recognizing Patterns and Cycles		♦	♦	♦	♦	♦
Identifying Cause and Effect Extending the Senses				♦	♦	♦
Designing and Conducting Controlled Experiments						♦

research findings about children's learning. These findings indicate that knowledge is actively constructed by each learner and that children learn science best in a hands-on experimental environment where they can make their own discoveries. The steps of the learning cycle are as follows:

- Focus: Explore and clarify the ideas that children already have about the topic.

- Explore: Enable children to engage in hands-on explorations of the objects, organisms, and science phenomena to be investigated.

- Reflect: Encourage children to discuss their observations and to reconcile their ideas.

- Apply: Help children discuss and apply their new ideas in new situations.

The learning cycle in STC units gives students opportunities to develop increased understanding of important scientific concepts and to develop positive attitudes toward science.

The STC units provide teachers with a variety of strategies with which to assess student learning. The STC units also offer teachers opportunities to link the teaching of science with the development of skills in mathematics, language arts, and social studies. In addition, the STC units encourage the use of cooperative learning to help students develop the valuable skill of working together.

In the extensive research and development process used with all STC units, scientists and educators, including experienced elementary school teachers, act as consultants to teacher-developers, who research, trial teach, and write the units. The process begins with the developer researching the unit's content and pedagogy. Then, before writing the unit, the developer trial teaches lessons in public school classrooms in the metropolitan Washington, D.C., area. Once a unit is written, the NSRC evaluates its effectiveness with children by field-testing it nationally in ethnically diverse urban, rural, and suburban public schools. At the field-testing stage, the assessment sections in each unit are also evaluated by the Program Evaluation and Research Group of Lesley College, located in Cambridge, Mass. The final editions of the units reflect the incorporation of teacher and student field-test feedback and of comments on accuracy and soundness from the leading scientists and science educators who serve on the STC Advisory Panel.

The STC project would not have been possible without the generous support of numerous federal agencies, private foundations, and corporations. Supporters include the National Science Foundation, the Smithsonian Institution, the U.S. Department of Defense, the U.S. Department of Education, the John D. and Catherine T. MacArthur Foundation, the Dow Chemical Company Foundation, the Amoco Foundation, Inc., E. I. du Pont de Nemours & Company, the Hewlett-Packard Company, the Smithsonian Institution Educational Outreach Fund, and the Smithsonian Women's Committee.

Acknowledgments

Rocks and Minerals was researched and developed by Don Cammiso and Joyce Lowry Weiskopf (STC Project Director, 1992–95). Following field-testing, the unit was revised by Dr. Weiskopf. It was edited by Linda Harteker and illustrated by Max-Karl Winkler. Other NSRC staff who contributed to the development and production of this unit include Charles N. Hardy, deputy director for information dissemination, materials development, and publications (1995–96); Dean Trackman, publications director; and Heidi M. Kupke, publications technology specialist. The unit was evaluated by Sabra Lee, senior research associate, Program Evaluation and Research Group, Lesley College. *Rocks and Minerals* was trial taught with Nancy Jacobs in her third-grade classroom at Sully Elementary School, Loudoun County Public Schools, Sterling, Virginia.

The technical review of *Rocks and Minerals* was conducted by:

Robert Ridky, Associate Professor of Geology, University of Maryland, College Park, MD

Gregory Holden, Professor of Geological Engineering, Colorado School of Mines, Golden, CO

The NSRC would like to thank the following individuals and school systems for their assistance with the national field-testing of the unit:

Bozeman Public Schools, Bozeman, MT
Coordinator: Ned Levine, Principal, Willson Science and Technology School
Susan Backer, Teacher, Longfellow School
Sue Livers, Teacher, Willson Science and Technology School
John Usher, Teacher, Emily Dickinson School

Fairfax County Public Schools, Fairfax, VA
Coordinator: Debbie Jones, Science Specialist
Greg Alexander, Teacher, Weyanoke Elementary School
Tish Beacham, Teacher, North Springfield Elementary School
Mary Ann Rogers, Teacher, Great Falls Elementary School

San Francisco Unified School District, San Francisco, CA
Coordinator: Anna Huie
Sandra DeGroot, Teacher, West Portal School

Andrea Gormley, Teacher, McKinley School
May Lui, Teacher, Cabrillo Elementary School

Sheboygan Area School District, Sheboygan, WI
Coordinator: Jerry Doyle, Coordinator of Mathematics and Science
Chris Halverson, Teacher, Longfellow Elementary School
Margaret Heyn, Teacher, Cooper Elementary School
Karen Urban, Teacher, Grant Elementary School

The NSRC also would like to thank the following individuals for their contributions to the unit:

Harold H. Banks, National Museum of Natural History, Smithsonian Institution, Washington, DC
Janet Brown, Postdoctoral Researcher, School of Education, University of California, Santa Barbara, CA
Susan Browning, Principal, Sully Elementary School, Loudoun County Public Schools, Sterling, VA
Valda Kirkwood, Professor, Science Education, Melbourne University, Melbourne, Australia
Dane Penland, Chief, Imaging and Technology Services Branch, Office of Imaging, Printing, and Photographic Services, Smithsonian Institution, Washington, DC
David Schindel, Senior Adviser, Office of Science and Technology Infrastructure, National Science Foundation, Arlington, VA
Richard Shavelson, Professor, School of Education, University of California, Santa Barbara, CA
Susan Snyder, Program Director, Teacher Enhancement, National Science Foundation, Arlington, VA
Richard Strauss, Photographer, Office of Imaging, Printing, and Photographic Services, Smithsonian Institution, Washington, DC
Jeff Tinsley, Chief, Special Assignments/Photography Branch, Office of Imaging, Printing, and Photographic Services, Smithsonian Institution, Washington, DC
Rick Vargas, Photographer, Office of Imaging, Printing, and Photographic Services, Smithsonian Institution, Washington, DC

The NSRC is indebted to all of the above individuals, who were instrumental in ensuring the scientific accuracy and pedagogical usefulness of the learning activities in this unit.

Sally Goetz Shuler
Executive Director
National Science Resources Center

STC Advisory Panel

National Science Resources Center

Douglas Lapp, Executive Director
Sally Goetz Shuler, Deputy Director for Development,
  External Relations, and Outreach
R. Gail Thomas, Administrative Officer
Gail Greenberg, Executive Administrative Assistant
Dorothy Smith, Administrative Assistant

Publications
Dean Trackman, Director
Marilyn Fenichel, Managing Editor, STC Discovery Deck
Linda Harteker, Writer/Editor
Lynn Miller, Writer/Editor
Dorothy Sawicki, Writer/Editor
Max-Karl Winkler, Illustrator
Heidi M. Kupke, Publications Technology Specialist
Matthew Smith, Editorial Assistant
Laura Akgulian, Writer/Editor Consultant
Cynthia Allen, Writer/Editor Consultant
Judith Grumstrup-Scott, Writer/Editor Consultant
Lois Sloan, Illustrator Consultant

Science and Technology for Children Project
Patricia K. Freitag, Director
Judith White, Program Officer, STC Discovery Deck
Wendy Binder, Research Associate
Carol O'Donnell, Research Associate
Lisa Bevell, Program Assistant
Amanda Revere, Program Aide

Outreach
Linda J. Bentley, Outreach Coordinator
Leslie J. Benton, Program Officer, Technical Assistance
Julie Clyman Lee, Program Associate

Information Dissemination
Evelyn M. Ernst, Director
Rita C. Warpeha, Resource/Database Specialist
Barbara K. Johnson, Research Associate
Sarah Lanning, Program Assistant

The above individuals were members of the NSRC staff in 1996.

Science Notebooks in the STC Classroom

Writing is one of the ways that children learn in science. . . . When children explain what they have seen and why they think this occurs in writing, they are forced to clarify their thoughts and organize these ideas in a way that others can understand.

Jenny Feely
"Writing in Science"
in *Science & Language Links*

Every student in an STC classroom should be required to keep a science notebook. Students in grades 3 through 6 can use a loose-leaf binder or a composition book for this purpose; first- and second-graders write directly in their consumable STC Student Notebooks. Students should keep their notebooks with them throughout science class, so that they can add entries daily and review their notes as the unit progresses. Teachers are encouraged to review students' notebook entries periodically to assess their progress in recording the results of their investigations and the growth in their understanding of important concepts.

Why Is a Science Notebook Important?

Science notebooks are important for many reasons. The first reason is that writing is an integral part of the process of learning science. By using notebooks, students model one of the most vital and enduring functions of scientists in all disciplines—recording data. Scientists across the world record their observations and conclusions, as well as comments on their readings and reflections. They rely on their notes when sharing their findings with peers and when preparing the papers in which they share their work with the broader scientific community. The notebooks of famous scientists such as Galileo and Albert Einstein have become part of the world's cultural heritage.

A second reason for maintaining a science notebook is that it provides the student with a ready reference during the unit as well as a resource to consult when reviewing materials at the end of the unit. The notebook is also a means of communicating with other students and with the teacher.

A science notebook encourages the students' creativity. Students are encouraged to draw as well as to write in their notebooks. Keeping a notebook also enhances students' writing skills. It gives them practice in organizing materials and in expressing themselves clearly. At the same time, notebook writing can encourage students to connect science with other areas of the curriculum. Extensions in the STC units, for example, ask students to write poems, stories, or songs, or to do research in related areas such as history and geography.

Another advantage of notebooks is that they get students more involved in science. Students take ownership of their notebooks. As the unit progresses, they have a growing sense of pride in what they have written and learned. Their confidence in their science learning, as well as in their overall knowledge and skills, grows.

Finally, the science notebook offers the teacher a unique means of assessing student progress in science learning. The notebook, ideally begun during the first lesson of the unit and continued to its conclusion, is a tool that can be used to assess the growth in students' understanding of science as well as in their ability to summarize and capture their findings.

Science notebooks are tools for inquiry that allow children to frame questions and seek answers. . . . They are to be used to identify student understanding and misconceptions about science concepts and to inform further practice.

Science Notebook Guidebook
Cambridge Public Schools
Cambridge, Mass.

Incorporating Science Notebooks Into Classroom Activity

Making time for students to write in their notebooks daily can be challenging. With proper planning, however, writing becomes a natural part of the rhythm of the science class.

When to Write

The time at which writing is done depends on the nature of the classroom activity on a given day and on the teacher's choice. What is most important is that students have sufficient time to write, and that they have an opportunity to write in their notebooks daily.

During some inquiries, things may go more smoothly if students suspend their hands-on investigations at certain points, write in their notebooks, and then resume their activity. In other cases, the best time to write is after the inquiry ends. Teachers should allow time for students to share their writing with their peers and the entire class.

Even though students have used their notebooks repeatedly during a lesson, time should always be left at the end of a lesson for students to reflect on what they have learned and to write down any new questions that have arisen.

Notebook Materials

Student notebook materials are diverse. Students may use a bound composition book or a loose-leaf notebook; they can even staple sheets of construction paper around blank or lined paper. Many teachers prefer loose-leaf notebooks because they are more flexible. Folders with pockets and fasteners for three-hole paper also work well because they provide storage space for record sheets, graph paper, and other materials. Other teachers prefer composition books, which deter students from removing or deleting past recordings. Students can glue or tape their record sheets into the composition books.

Notebook Organization

Teachers should make sure that all the students in the class organize their notebooks in the same way. The notebooks should, for example, begin with a table of contents. Students can allow several pages for this at the beginning of the unit. As they begin each lesson, students can then add the title of the lesson to their table of contents. Students should always date their entries and number the pages consecutively throughout the unit. Tabs can help students organize their notebooks and locate specific sections more easily.

Getting Started

Students who have not used science notebooks may need some initial guidance on how to use them most effectively.

You might want to begin by facilitating a brainstorming session designed to increase students' awareness of the importance of maintaining a notebook. Then present some guidelines such as those noted in the previous section.

Tell students that you will be looking at the notebooks often to see how they are doing. At the same time, emphasize that the notebook is primarily for their own benefit. Stress that they should write down not only facts and observations but also questions and ideas they want to further explore.

Help them understand that they should use their notebooks in two major ways. First, they should "take notes" on what they have seen, experienced, and concluded. As they move through the investigation, students should also "make notes"—that is, ask questions and pose comments. Emphasize the importance of always writing clearly and of expressing thoughts in an organized way.

Urge students to use drawings as well as text. They should also be encouraged to design tables and graphs to display findings.

Explain that when you look at the notebooks, you will consider many things. You will look at how complete their entries are. You will also try to determine how much effort they have put into their answers and questions. For a science notebook, this is more important than the "right" answers. Students should think of the information in their notebooks as a rough draft; therefore, you will not assess them on the basis of style, correct spelling, or word usage. The notebooks should, however, be neat and clearly written. The notes that scientists keep must be readable by other scientists, and students' notebooks should meet this same standard.

Organizing the Notebooks

When talking about a good way to organize the notebooks, you might also tell students that the information they write down should be a record of the basic components of their scientific inquiry. These steps are as follows:

- The question that the student wants to answer

- A prediction about how the inquiry will turn out

- The student's plan for the inquiry and the materials that he or she will use

- The student's data and observations (includes words, tables and graphs, and illustrations)

- The student's conclusions

■ Next steps or new questions that have arisen from the inquiry

STC lessons generally end with a discussion, during which students share their findings and suggest additional questions to explore. When the discussion ends, you may ask students to return to their notebooks and to summarize, in their own words, the major ideas that have emerged during this discussion. Have students separate these final comments from their previous notes by a horizontal line, which is called the "line of learning."

Keeping a Science Notebook: Student Objectives

After sufficient practice, students who keep science notebooks should be able to do the following:

■ Increase their understanding of science concepts.

■ Use writing as a process for discovery.

■ Improve their ability to organize ideas and information.

■ Recognize the connection between thinking and writing.

■ Write more freely, more comfortably, and more often.

Adapted from
"Writing for Understanding"
in *Science and Writing Connections*

Reviewing Science Notebooks

Check the students' science notebooks often. Glance at the notebooks during class and collect them periodically for a more detailed review.

You may give feedback to students in many ways. Some teachers prefer to use Post-it Notes™; others write on the notebook page itself; others may prefer to enter their comments in the back of the book. Use a color that is distinguishable from the black or blue that students generally use (green is one idea); it's best not to use red ink. Some teachers ask students to bring their tape recorders to school so they make their comments into the recorder.

Make your feedback positive and constructive. Grade students for the completeness of their work and for their effort. Do not grade ideas as "right" or "wrong." Misspellings or grammatical

errors should not be circled or criticized in the notebook. Date and initial all your written comments.

To bring objectivity to the assessment process, some teachers use rubrics. A simple assessment rubric is as follows:

Rubric for Assessing Science Notebooks

STANDARD	SCORE
Date and purpose of inquiry	
Appropriate prediction	
List of materials	
Sequence of procedures	
Diagrams and labels	
Chart or data table as it corresponds to student's results	
Conclusions as they relate to data and answers to the inquiry questions	

3 = Achieved the standard with honors.
2 = Achieved the standard.
1 = Achievement below the standard.
0 = No evidence of achievement.

Conclusion

Student notebooks fill many roles. They promote students' science learning and give students an opportunity to enhance their writing skills. They help students better appreciate the process of scientific inquiry. They help students organize their learning and, by the end of the unit, realize how much they have learned. For teachers, notebooks are a unique means of reviewing student learning.

These guidelines should help you and your students take full advantage of the many benefits that student science notebooks bring to the STC classroom.

Acknowledgment

The NSRC thanks the Cambridge Public Schools and Beckman@Science for providing materials on writing and assessing student science notebooks.

References
Reading
Baker, L., Dreher, M.J., and Guthrie, J. *Engaging Young Readers*. New York: Guilford Publications, Inc. 2000.

Gaskins, I., Guthrie, J., et al. Integrating instruction of science, reading, and writing: Goals, teacher development, and assessment. *Journal of Research in Science Teaching*, 31, 1039-1056. 1994.

Guthrie, J. Educational contexts for engagement in literacy. *The Reading Teacher*, 49, 432-445. 1996.

Guthrie, J., Anderson, E., Alao, S., and Rinehart, J. Influences of concept-oriented reading instruction on strategy use and conceptual learning from text. *The Elementary School Journal*, 99, 343-366. 1999.

Guthrie, J., Cox, K., et al. Principles of integrated instruction for engagement in reading. *Educational Psychology Review*, 10, 177-199. 1998.

Guthrie, J. T., Van Meter, P., Hancock, G.R., et al. Does concept-oriented reading instruction increase strategy use and conceptual learning from text? *Journal of Educational Psychology*, 90, 261-278. 1998.

Palinscar, A.S., and Brown, A.L. Reciprocal teaching of comprehension-fostering and comprehension-monitoring activities. *Cognition and Instruction*, 1(2), 117-175. 1984.

Romance, N., and Vitale, M. A curriculum strategy that expands time for in-depth elementary science instruction by using science-based reading strategies: Effects of a year-long study in grade four. *Journal of Research in Science Teaching*, 29, 545-554. 1992.

Science Notebook Writing

Baxter, G., Bass, K., and Glaser, R. Notebook writing in three fifth-grade science classrooms. *The Elementary School Journal*. 2001.

Beckman@Science. *Introduction to Science Notebooks*. Irvine, Calif.

Cambridge Science Department, Cambridge Public Schools. *Science Notebook Guidebook*. Cambridge, Mass. 2001.

Feely, Jenny. Writing in science. In: Scott, J. *Science & Language Links: Classroom Implications*. Portsmouth, N.H.: Heinemann. 1993.

Freedman, R.L.H. *Science and Writing Connections*. Palo Alto, Calif.: Dale Seymour Publications. 1999.

Keys, C.W. Revitalizing instruction in the scientific genres: Connecting knowledge production with writing to learn in science. *Science Education*, 83, 115-130. 1999.

Klentschy, M., Garrison, L., and Amaral, O.M. (1999). Valle Imperial Project in Science (VIPS) Four-Year Comparison of Student Achievement Data 1995–1999. El Centro, Calif. 1999.

National Council of Teachers of English and The International Reading Association. *Standards for the English Language Arts*. Urbana, Ill.: NCTE. 1996.

Shepardson, D.P., and Britsch, S.J. Children's science journals: Tools for teaching, learning, and assessing. *Science and Children*, 34, 13-7; 46-47. 1997.

Reif, R.J., and Rauch, K. Science in their own words. *Science and Children*, 31, 31-33. 1994.

Daniels, H. *Literature Circles, Voice and Choice in the Student-Centered Classroom*. York, Maine: Stenhouse Publishers. 1994.

Contents

Goals for *Rocks and Minerals*

In this unit, students investigate rocks and minerals. Through their experiences, students are introduced to the following concepts, skills, and attitudes.

Concepts

- Rocks are aggregates of minerals, and they may also contain organic matter.

- Different rocks have different properties.

- The properties of rocks reflect the way they were formed and the minerals in them.

- Each mineral is composed of only one substance, and that substance is the same in all samples of the mineral.

- Minerals differ in color, texture, smell, luster, transparency, hardness, shape, and reaction to magnets.

- The properties of rocks and minerals determine how they are used.

Skills

- Using senses to observe and describe rocks and minerals.

- Recording and discussing observations of rocks and minerals.

- Sorting minerals on the basis of similarities and differences in identified properties.

- Performing and interpreting results of the following tests on minerals: streak, transparency, luster, hardness, and magnetism.

- Recording and discussing results of tests on minerals.

- Reading for more information on minerals and rocks.

- Communicating observations and test results through writing and discussion.

- Reflecting on experiences through writing and discussion.

- Applying previously learned concepts and skills to solve a problem.

Attitudes

- Developing an interest in investigating rocks and minerals.

- Recognizing the importance of using multiple tests to create a profile of a mineral.

- Valuing scientific information that has been collected and verified over time.

(AFJ), (AGI), (AHK), (ABE), (ALR)

(BGK), ~~BFL~~, (BIJ), ~~BAE~~

(DHL), (DEJ), (DGM), (DIR), (DFK)

(EIM), ~~EDJ~~, (EFR), ~~EAB~~

~~FAJ~~, ~~FBE~~, ~~FER~~, (FHM), ~~FDK~~

~~GBK~~, ~~GAI~~, ~~GDM~~, (GJL)

~~HDL~~, (HKR), ~~HAK~~, ~~HFM~~

~~IFM~~, ~~IAG~~, ~~IBJ~~, ~~IDR~~, (IKL)

~~JAF~~, ~~JDE~~, ~~JBE~~, ~~JGL~~, (JMR)

~~KBG~~, ~~KAR~~, ~~KAH~~, ~~BKDF~~, ~~KIL~~

~~LDH~~, ~~LBF~~, ~~LGJ~~, ~~LIK~~, ~~LAR~~

~~MEI~~, ~~MDG~~, ~~MFH~~, ~~MJR~~

~~RHK~~, ~~REF~~, ~~RDI~~, ~~RAL~~, ~~RJH~~

20 combos #1 (AFJ) 6 BGK 9 DHL 14 EIM 16 FHM 17 GJL 18 AKR

2 AGI 7 BFL 10 DEJ 15 EFR

3 AHK 8 BIJ 11 DGM

4 ABE   12 DIR   19 (IKL) 20 JMR

5 ALR   13 DFK

4 A̲ |||| H |||| B̶

B |||| 4 I̲ ||||

D |||| 4 J̲ ||||

E |||| 4 K̲ ||||

4 F |||| 4 L̲ ||||

G |||| M ||||

          R ||||

Unit Overview and Materials List

Most children have picked up a rock or mineral to show their parents or friends. Some children may even have found a crystal or fossil. Children often collect and sort rocks and minerals; they also may trade them with friends. They are fascinated with the colors, sizes, and textures of rocks and minerals they find as well as of those they see in museums and rock shops. This natural interest, coupled with the variety of rocks and minerals, leads many children to wonder what these earth materials are made of and how they were formed.

Rocks and Minerals is a 16-lesson unit in which third-graders investigate rocks and minerals to answer these and other questions. Students explore the similarities and differences among rocks; they also study how rocks and minerals are both similar and different. They conduct several tests on minerals and develop a systematic way to record their observations. Finally, students apply the information they have collected to identify the minerals they have been studying by name. These activities introduce students to the way geologists study rocks and minerals. They also help students develop and apply process skills in observing, describing, and recording.

Lesson 1 begins with a class brainstorming session during which students share what they know about rocks and the questions they have about them. As they observe and describe three rocks, students are introduced to one of the key concepts of this unit—that rocks have different *properties.* This lesson serves as a pre-unit assessment of students' present thinking about rocks. It also provides baseline information that the teacher may use to assess students' observing, describing, and recording skills.

In Lessons 2 and 3, students explore the properties of the three rocks they examined in Lesson 1 as well as nine new ones. After sorting these rocks on the basis of their observable properties, they read about where rocks are found and how they are formed. The reading acquaints them with the concept that rocks can change as a result of heat or pressure. The

experiences in these two lessons deepen students' appreciation of the diversity of rocks.

Lesson 4 broadens the students' investigations of earth materials by introducing them to minerals. After exploring three mineral samples, students examine their rocks with a hand lens and look for small pieces of minerals. Through this experience, students are introduced to the concept that minerals are the "building blocks" of rocks.

In Lesson 5, students receive a set of 12 minerals, labeled "A" to "L." They examine the minerals and discuss their observations with their partners and classmates. Students also share what they know about minerals and the questions they have about them. This activity provides a second opportunity to assess their prior knowledge.

In Lessons 6 to 12, students explore the minerals to learn more about their properties. They perform a series of physical and chemical tests, called "field tests," that geologists use to identify and classify minerals. The students describe their results to their partners and classmates and systematically record their observations on 12 mineral profile sheets. As they perform the tests, students have an opportunity to learn how to manipulate science materials. They also acquire new vocabulary related to the study of minerals.

The field tests that students perform are of varying degrees of complexity, beginning with simple tests and moving on to more challenging ones. In Lesson 6, students use their senses to explore the feel and smell of the 12 minerals. In Lessons 7 to 10, they move on to test and record the observable and identifying colors, transparency, luster, and hardness of each mineral. In Lesson 11, they test each mineral's magnetism. These explorations conclude in Lesson 12, where students focus on the shape of minerals. After each test, students read about one or two minerals that display a distinctive result for the test that they have just performed.

In Lesson 13, students review the information they have recorded on their mineral profile sheets and identify the properties that helped them learn the most about each mineral. After summarizing these properties, students examine and compare several samples of each mineral. These observations broaden their understanding that even though mineral share certain properties, individual samples can look quite different from one another. In Lesson 14, students compare the information they have recorded about each mineral with that provided by a geologist on mineral identification cards. Applying all the information they have accumulated, students match each mineral sample to the appropriate card and thereby identify the minerals by name. As a final activity, they combine their mineral profile sheets and the mineral identification cards to make their own "Minerals Field Guides."

In Lesson 15, students are challenged with an application assessment. They are given three "mystery minerals" and three blank mineral profile sheets. They apply the field tests of their choice to learn as much as they can about each mineral. Using all the information they have acquired during their exploration of minerals and their "Mineral Field Guides," students then compare the three new minerals with those they have studied previously.

The unit concludes by giving students the opportunity to make the connection between minerals and rocks and to explore their uses. Students learn that minerals are obtained from rocks. Using guided and independent research, they prepare reports on a rock or mineral that interests them. Students' oral presentations of these reports provide an opportunity for a final assessment of the knowledge they have gained from their study of earth materials.

Throughout *Rocks and Minerals*, students have many opportunities to observe the similarities and differences in properties of minerals and rocks and to gather, organize, and interpret data. They discover that the application of scientific techniques can provide them with useful information about rocks and minerals. As they perform the field tests and discuss the results, students become engaged in a process that encourages problem solving and fosters understanding of the concept that scientific results cannot always be reported with "yes-or-no" answers.

Materials List

Listed below are the materials needed for teaching *Rocks and Minerals* to 30 students. Please note that metric and English equivalents in this unit are only approximate.

1   *Rocks and Minerals* Teacher's Guide

15   *Rocks and Minerals* Student Activity Books

16   samples of each of the following numbered rocks:
1. granite
2. gneiss
3. conglomerate
4. limestone (fossiliferous)
5. shale
6. sandstone (pink with layers)
7. obsidian
8. basalt
9. pumice
10. slate
11. marble
12. schist (with garnet)

16   samples of each of the following lettered minerals:
A. feldspar
B. quartz (displaying hexagonal form)
C. galena (displaying cubic form)
D. calcite (Icelandic spar variety)
E. fluorite
F. graphite
G. hematite (black specular variety)
H. gypsum (massive form/alabaster)
I. magnetite
J. muscovite
K. sulfur (crystalline)
L. talc
M. halite
N. gypsum (massive and fibrous/satin spar variety)
O. gypsum (bladed selenite crystal aggregate in "desert rose" form)
P. quartz (pink massive crystals)
Q. hematite (red variety)
R. biotite
S. gypsum (clear selenite crystal)

8   boxes of plastic disposable gloves

35   plastic containers with lids, 0.5 liter (1 pt)

30   hand lenses

15   flexible magnets, 25 × 20 × 5 mm (1 × 1 × ¼ in)

15   cardboard trays

15   white porcelain streak plates

15   black porcelain streak plates

15   penlights with batteries

15   steel nails, size 12

15   droppers

15   plastic cups, 90 ml (3 oz)

1   roll waxed paper

3   sheets of transparent film

*15   egg cartons

*15   copper pennies

*1   roll of clear tape

*1   roll of masking tape

*   Newsprint pad, 61 × 91 cm (24 × 36 in)

*15   pieces of manila paper, 10 × 15 cm (4 × 6 in)

*   Cardboard, enough for 15 75-mm (3-in) squares

*1   pad of Post-it® notes, 76 × 127 mm (3 × 5 in)

*   Colored markers

*   Assorted crayons or colored pencils

*   Glue

*   Stapler

*   Scissors

*   Old newspapers

*   Paper towels

*   Dish detergent

*   Liquid tile cleaner

*   Small bucket

Note: These items are not included in the kit. They are commonly available in most schools or can be brought from home.

Teaching *Rocks and Minerals*

The following information on unit structure, teaching strategies, materials, and assessment will help you give students the guidance they need to make the most of their hands-on experiences with this unit.

Unit Structure

How Lessons Are Organized in the Teacher's Guide: Each lesson in the *Rocks and Minerals* Teacher's Guide provides you with a brief overview, lesson objectives, key background information, a materials list, advance preparation instructions, step-by-step procedures, and helpful management tips. Many of the lessons include recommended guidelines for assessment. Lessons also frequently indicate opportunities for curriculum integration. Look for the following icons that highlight extension ideas:

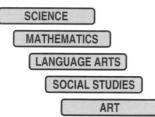

Please note that all record sheets, blackline masters, student instructions, and reading selections may be copied and used in conjunction with the teaching of this unit. For purposes of classroom use only, you may make an overhead transparency of a specific page or item in the Teacher's Guide or Student Activity Book.

Student Activity Book: The *Rocks and Minerals* Student Activity Book accompanies the Teacher's Guide. Written specifically for students, this activity book contains simple instructions and illustrations to enable students to conduct the activities in this unit. The Student Activity Book will help students follow along with you as you guide each lesson. It will also provide guidance for students who may miss a lesson or for those who do not immediately grasp certain activities or concepts. In addition to previewing each lesson in the Teacher's Guide, you may find it helpful to preview the accompanying lesson in the Student Activity Book.

The lessons in the Student Activity Book are divided into the following sections, paralleling the Teacher's Guide:

- **Think and Wonder** sketches for students a general picture of the ideas and activities of the lesson described in the **Overview and Objectives** of the Teacher's Guide.

- **Materials** lists the materials students and their partners or teammates will be using.

- **Find Out for Yourself** flows in tandem with the steps in the **Procedure** and **Final Activities** sections of the Teacher's Guide and briefly and simply walks students through the lesson's activities.

- **Ideas to Explore,** which echoes many of the activities in the **Extensions** section in the Teacher's Guide, gives students additional activities to try out or ideas to think about.

Teaching Strategies

Classroom Discussion: Class discussions, effectively led by the teacher, are important vehicles for science learning. Research shows that the way questions are asked, as well as the time allowed for responses, can contribute to the quality of the discussion.

When you ask questions, think about what you want to achieve in the ensuing discussion. For example, open-ended questions, for which there is no one right answer, will encourage students to give creative and thoughtful answers. You can use other types of questions to encourage students to see specific relationships and contrasts or to help them summarize and draw conclusions. It is good practice to mix these questions. It also is good practice always to give students "wait time" before expecting them to answer; this will encourage broader participation and more thoughtful answers. You will want to monitor responses, looking for additional situations that invite students to formulate hypotheses, make generalizations, and explain how they arrived at a conclusion.

Brainstorming: Brainstorming is a whole-class exercise in which students contribute their thoughts about a particular idea or problem. When used to introduce a new science topic, it can be a stimulating and productive exercise. It also is a useful and efficient way for the teacher to find out what students know and think about a topic. As students learn the rules for brainstorming, they will become increasingly adept in their participation.

To begin a brainstorming session, define for students the topics about which they will share ideas. Explain the following rules to students:

- Accept all ideas without judgment.

- Do not criticize or make unnecessary comments about the contributions of others.

- Try to connect your ideas to the ideas of others.

Cooperative Learning Groups: One of the best ways to teach hands-on science is to arrange students in small groups. Materials and procedures for *Rocks and Minerals* are based on groups of two. There are several advantages to this organization. It provides a small forum for students to express their ideas and get feedback. It also offers students a chance to learn from each other by sharing ideas, discoveries, and skills. With coaching, students can develop important interpersonal skills that will serve them well in all aspects of life. As students work, they will often find it productive to talk about what they are doing, resulting in a steady hum of conversation. If you or others in the school are accustomed to a quiet room, this busy atmosphere may require some adjustment.

Venn Diagrams: The Venn diagram is a useful tool for sorting, classifying, and comparing information. It will be used in three lessons of the *Rocks and Minerals* unit. You will make the first circle of the Venn diagram in Lesson 4, where students summarize their ideas about rocks. In Lesson 13, you will make the second circle of Venn diagram to summarize students' ideas about minerals. You will complete the Venn diagram by connecting the two circles in Lesson 16, when students compare the properties of rocks and minerals. Properties common to rocks and minerals will appear in the area where the circles intersect.

Learning Centers: You can give supplemental science materials a permanent home in the classroom in a spot designated as the learning center. Students will probably bring in samples of rocks and minerals they have found. You can place the students' samples in this area. Students can also use the center as an "on your own" project center, as an observation post, as a trade-book reading nook, or simply as a place to spend unscheduled time when assignments are done. To keep interest in the center high, change the learning center or add to it often. You might want to include a set of testing materials, science trade books (see the **Bibliography**), and magazine and newspaper articles about rocks and minerals.

Materials

Safety Notes: This unit does not contain anything highly toxic, but common sense dictates that nothing be put in the mouth. In fact, it is good practice to tell your students that, in science class, materials are never tasted. Use your own judgment to caution students when they are about to perform a field test such as the hardness test, which requires a steel nail. Safety tips appear throughout the unit at places where a reminder to students may be warranted. See the box below for important information on handling the mineral galena.

Safety Rules for Handling Galena

Galena is a form of lead sulfide, a compound that commonly occurs in the earth's crust. An attractive mineral with interesting physical properties, galena is widely used in earth science classes.

The Environmental Health Center of the National Safety Council notes that lead is poisonous in all forms and that lead poisoning is cumulative. Lead sulfide, however, is less toxic than the more soluble lead compounds, such as lead acetate, lead chloride, and lead oxide. (National Safety Council's Environmental Writer Chemical Backgrounder Web site: http://www.nsc.org/ehc/ew/chems/leadcmp2.htm). The National Center for Environmental Health at the Centers for Disease Control and Prevention in Atlanta has indicated that skin contact with galena is not dangerous. Nonetheless, to avoid any potential ingestion, people should always wash their hands after handling galena.

continued on pg. 8

---

continued from pg. 7

We recommend that teachers take the following safety precautions when using the galena samples in the STC® *Rocks and Minerals* kit:

- Inform students that galena, like all compounds containing lead, is poisonous if it is taken internally.

- To reduce the risk of ingestion by hand-to-mouth contact, have students wear disposable plastic gloves when they handle galena.

- Tell students to wash their hands after handling galena.

- Allow students access to the galena samples only under direct supervision.

- Do not allow students to take galena samples out of the classroom.

Organization of Materials: To help ensure an orderly progression through the unit, you will need to establish a system for storing and distributing materials. Being prepared is the key to success. Here are a few suggestions:

- Familiarize yourself with the materials as soon as possible.

- Know which activity is scheduled and which materials will be used for it.

- Involve your students in distributing and returning the materials. If you have an existing network of cooperative groups, delegate the responsibility to one member of each group.

- Organize a distribution center and instruct your students to pick up and return supplies to that area. A cafeteria-style approach works especially well when there are large numbers of items to distribute.

- Look at each lesson ahead of time. Some have specific suggestions for handling materials needed that day.

- Management tips are provided throughout the unit. Look for the icon at the right.

Assessment

Philosophy: In the Science and Technology for Children program, assessment is an ongoing, integral part of instruction. Because assessment emerges naturally from the activities in the lessons, students are assessed in the same manner in which they are taught. They may, for example, perform experiments, record their observations, or make oral presentations. Such assessments permit the examination of processes as well as of products, emphasizing what students know and can do.

The learning goals in STC units include a number of different science concepts, skills, and attitudes. Therefore, a number of different strategies are provided to help you assess and document your students' progress toward the goals. These strategies also will help you report to parents and appraise your own teaching. In addition, the assessments will enable your students to view their own progress, reflect on their learning, and formulate further questions for investigation and research.

Figure T-1 summarizes the goals and assessment strategies for this unit. The left-hand column lists the individual goals for the *Rocks and Minerals* unit and the lessons in which they are addressed. The right-hand column identifies lessons containing assessment sections to which you can turn for specific assessment strategies. These strategies are summarized as bulleted items.

Assessment Strategies: The assessment strategies in STC units fall into three categories: matched pre- and post-unit assessments, embedded assessments, and additional assessments.

The first lesson of each STC unit is a *pre-unit assessment* designed to give you information about what the whole class and individual students already know about the unit's topic and what they want to find out. It often includes a brainstorming session during which students share their thoughts about the topic through exploring one or two basic questions. In the *post-unit assessment* following the final lesson, the class revisits the pre-unit assessment questions, giving you two sets of comparable data that indicate students' growth in knowledge and skills.

Throughout a unit, assessments are incorporated, or embedded, into lessons. These *embedded assessments* are activities that occur naturally within the context of both the individual lesson and the unit as a whole; they are often indistinguishable from instructional activities. By providing structured activities and guidelines for assessing students'

continued on pg. 11

Figure T-1

Rocks and Minerals: Goals and Assessment Strategies

Concepts	
Goals	**Assessment Strategies**
Rocks are aggregates of minerals, and they may also contain organic matter. Lessons 1–4, 16	Lessons 1, 5, 16 • Pre- and post-unit assessments • Notebooks • Brainstorming charts • Record sheets • Oral reports • Venn diagram
Different rocks have different properties. Lessons 1–4, 16	Lessons 1, 4, 16 • Pre- and post-unit assessments • Notebooks • Record sheets • Class discussions
The properties of rocks reflect the way they were formed and the minerals in them. Lessons 3–4, 16	Lessons 4–5, 16 • Pre- and post-unit assessments • Notebooks • Class discussions • Oral reports
Each mineral is composed of only one substance, and that substance is the same in all samples of the mineral. Lessons 5–15	Lessons 5, 13, 15 • Pre- and post-unit assessments • Notebooks • Mineral profile sheets • Individual and class discussions • Oral and written reports • Venn diagram
Minerals differ in color, texture, smell, luster, transparency, hardness, shape, and reaction to magnets. Lessons 6–15	Lessons 5–6, 13, 15 • Pre- and post-unit assessments • Mineral profile sheets • Notebooks • Individual and class discussions
The properties of rocks and minerals determine how they are used. Lessons 7–16	Lesson 16 • Oral and written reports

Skills	
Goals	**Assessment Strategies**
Using senses to observe and describe rocks and minerals. Lessons 1–16	Lessons 1, 4, 6, 13 • Record sheets • Mineral profile sheets • Individual and class discussions • Venn diagram
Recording and discussing observations of rocks and minerals. Lessons 1–16	Lessons 1, 4–6, 13, 15 • Notebooks • Record sheets • Mineral profile sheets • Individual and class discussions

Goals	Assessment Strategies
Sorting minerals on the basis of similarities and differences in identified properties. Lessons 6–14	Lessons 6, 13 ▪ Teacher's observations ▪ Mineral profile sheets ▪ Notebooks ▪ Class discussions
Performing and interpreting results of the following tests on minerals: streak, transparency, luster, hardness, and magnetism. Lessons 7–15	Lessons 6, 13, 15 ▪ Teacher's observations ▪ Mineral profile sheets ▪ Individual and small-group discussions
Recording and discussing results of tests on minerals. Lessons 7–15	Lessons 6, 13, 15 ▪ Mineral profile sheets ▪ Individual and small-group discussions
Reading for more information on minerals and rocks. Lessons 3, 5–16	Lessons 6, 13, 16 ▪ Oral and written reports ▪ Notebooks ▪ Class discussions
Communicating observations and test results through writing and discussion. Lessons 1–16	Lessons 1, 4, 6, 13, 15 ▪ Notebooks ▪ Record sheets ▪ Mineral profile sheets ▪ Small-group and class discussions
Reflecting on experiences through writing and discussion. Lessons 2–16	Lessons 6, 13, 15–16 ▪ Notebooks ▪ Class discussions ▪ Oral and written reports
Applying previously learned concepts and skills to solve a problem. Lessons 13–14	Lessons 13, 15 ▪ Teacher's observations ▪ Notebooks ▪ Small-group discussions

Attitudes	
Goals	**Assessment Strategies**
Developing an interest in investigating rocks and minerals. Lessons 1–16	Lessons 1, 16 ▪ Pre- and post-unit assessments ▪ Class discussions ▪ Student self-assessment
Recognizing the importance of using multiple tests to create a profile of a mineral. Lessons 9–16	Lessons 13–15 ▪ Notebooks ▪ Class discussions
Valuing scientific information that has been collected and verified over time. Lessons 13–16	Lessons 13, 15–16 ▪ Notebooks ▪ Oral and written reports ▪ Class discussions

continued from pg. 8

progress and thinking, embedded assessments contribute to an ongoing, detailed profile of growth. In many STC units, the last lesson is an embedded assessment that challenges students to synthesize and apply concepts or skills from the unit.

The study of properties in *Rocks and Minerals* follows a pattern in which students observe, describe, record, and discuss their findings. Specific guidelines for assessments are presented in the first and last lessons, at the end of the section on rocks (Lesson 4), at the beginning of the series of lessons on minerals (Lesson 5), and in Lesson 13. Lesson 15 is an embedded assessment of students' ability to apply previously learned information to three new minerals.

Additional assessments can be used to determine students' understanding after the unit has been completed. In these assessments, students may work with materials to solve problems, conduct experiments, or interpret and organize data. In grades three through six, they may also complete self-assessments or paper-and-pencil tests. When you are selecting additional assessments, consider using more than one assessment to give students with different learning styles opportunities to express their knowledge and skills. The *Rocks and Minerals* unit contains four suggestions for additional assessments.

Documenting Student Performance: In STC units, assessment is based on your recorded observations, students' work products, and oral communication. All these documentation methods combine to give you a comprehensive picture of each student's growth.

Teachers' *observations and anecdotal notes* often provide the most useful information about students' understanding, especially in the early grades when some students are not yet writing their ideas fluently. Because it is important to document observations used for assessment, teachers frequently keep note cards, journals, or checklists. Many lessons include guidelines to help you focus your observations. The blackline master on pg. 12 provides a format you may want to use or adapt for recording observations.

Work products, which include both what students write and what they make, indicate students' progress toward the goals of the unit. Children produce a variety of written materials during a unit. Record sheets, which include written observations, drawings, graphs, tables, and charts, are an important part of all STC units.

They provide evidence of each student's ability to collect, record, and process information. Students' science journals are another type of work product. In grades one and two, journal writings are primarily suggested as extension activities in many lessons. Often a rich source of information for assessment, these journal writings reveal students' thoughts, ideas, and questions over time.

Students' written work products should be kept together in folders to document learning over the course of the unit. When students refer back to their work from previous lessons, they can reflect on their learning. In some cases, students do not write or draw well enough for their products to be used for assessment purposes, but their experiences do contribute to the development of scientific literacy.

Oral communication—what students say formally and informally in class and in individual sessions with you—is a particularly useful way to learn what students know. This unit provides your students with many opportunities to share and discuss their own ideas, observations, and opinions. Some young children may be experiencing such activities for the first time. Encourage students to participate in discussions, and stress that there are no right or wrong responses. Creating an environment in which students feel secure expressing their own ideas can stimulate rich and diverse discussions.

Individual and group presentations can give you insights about the meanings your students have assigned to procedures and concepts and about their confidence in their learning. In fact, a student's verbal description of a chart, experiment, or graph is frequently more useful for assessment than the product or results. Questions posed by other students following presentations provide yet another opportunity for you to gather information. Ongoing records of discussions and presentations should be a part of your documentation of students' learning.

Glossary

The glossary for this unit is provided as an additional resource for both teachers and students. The definitions are *not* unit specific and are intended to apply across the STC curriculum. The definitions are provided to facilitate discussion and may serve to enhance other unit activities. *Under no circumstances should students be required to memorize the terms or definitions presented in the glossary.*

Rocks and Minerals: Observations of Student Performance

STUDENT'S NAME:

Concepts	Observations
• Rocks are aggregates of minerals, and they may also contain organic matter. • Different rocks have different properties. • The properties of rocks reflect the way they were formed and the minerals in them. • Each mineral is composed of only one substance, and that substance is the same in all samples of the mineral. • Minerals differ in color, texture, smell, luster, transparency, hardness, shape, and reaction to magnets. • The properties of rocks and minerals determine how they are used.	
Skills • Using senses to observe and describe rocks and minerals. • Recording and discussing observations of rocks and minerals. • Sorting minerals on the basis of similarities and differences in identified properties. • Performing and interpreting results of the following tests on minerals: streak, transparency, luster, hardness, and magnetism. • Recording and discussing results of tests on minerals. • Reading for more information on minerals and rocks. • Communicating observations and test results through writing and discussion. • Reflecting on experiences through writing and discussion. • Applying previously learned concepts and skills to solve a problem.	

Sharing What We Know about Rocks

Overview and Objectives

Most children are interested in rocks. The brainstorming and class discussions in this introductory lesson acknowledge that interest and offer students an opportunity to share their ideas and questions about rocks. These activities serve as a pre-unit assessment of students' knowledge about rocks. As they explore three rocks and discuss their similarities and differences, students will provide information that you can use to assess their observing, describing, and recording skills. The activities also introduce students to the concept of properties and prepare them for further exploration of rocks in Lessons 2 and 3.

- Students set up science notebooks in which they will record their observations, ideas, and questions.

- Students share their ideas about rocks and discuss what they would like to learn about them.

- Students observe three rocks and record their descriptions of them.

- Students discuss their observations of rocks with their classmates.

- Students connect their descriptions of rocks with the properties of rocks.

Background

Most people refer to any earth material they pick up as a "rock." Rocks, however, are usually aggregates of minerals. Because of this, minerals are sometimes called the "building blocks" of rocks. Rocks may contain fossils, the remains of trees and other plants, animals, or compacted shells.

The mineral content of a rock helps determine its value. Geologists study rocks and minerals because of their value to society and because they can provide information about the history and formation of our earth.

The features geologists study when they classify rocks are called physical properties. **Properties** are those characteristics of matter that can be used to describe it. **Physical properties** are characteristics of an object that can be observed without altering its composition. The greater the number of unique properties an object has, the easier it is to identify. When two or more objects have similar properties, they sometimes must be examined carefully before being identified. This examination usually involves performing physical and chemical tests. When geologists are out in the field, they study the properties of rock samples by using observations and simple physical and chemical tests, called **field tests,** some of which students will learn in this unit.

The three rocks students explore in this lesson are granite, gneiss, and conglomerate. You may find it helpful to examine three or four samples of each of these rocks before you teach the lesson. **Granite** is a very hard rock formed deep within the earth when a molten mixture called **magma** cools rapidly to form solid mineral grains. Granite is composed primarily of the minerals quartz and feldspar. **Gneiss** (pronounced "nice") is a coarse, grainy rock formed from other rocks such as granite and sandstone that were changed underground by extreme heat and pressure. Granite and gneiss share many properties. It may be hard to tell them apart; in fact, one pun among geologists is "Don't take gneiss for granite!" **Conglomerate** is formed from coarse fragments of other rocks that have been released by weathering and transported by water to a site of accumulation. Conglomerate frequently looks like a chunk of concrete. Students will learn about these rocks and nine others in Lessons 1–3 and in Lesson 16. In Lessons 4–15, they will focus on minerals.

This first lesson, like the entire unit, is designed to increase your students' knowledge of rocks and minerals, to develop their process skills in observing, describing, and recording properties, and to give them an opportunity to apply their knowledge and skills to the study of new rocks and minerals. The names of rocks and minerals, as well as the terms used to describe their properties and the processes through which they were formed, are useful communication tools. Some students may be eager to learn all of the names and terms; others may not. It is important to remember that the use of scientific terminology and spelling should always **follow** exploration of the concepts. The ability to name does not indicate that learning has occurred—in other words, "naming isn't knowing." The use of scientific terminology is not a focus of this unit. Please refer to pgs. 6–12 in this guide for additional information on the assessment of students' learning.

Materials

For each student

  1   science notebook, with pockets and fasteners for loose-leaf paper
  1   **Record Sheet 1-A: Rocks—Record of My Observations**
  1   hand lens

For every two students

  1   *Rocks and Minerals* Student Activity Book
  1   set of three rocks, labeled 1–3
  1   cardboard tray

For the class

  4   sheets of newsprint, 60 × 90 cm (24 × 36 in)
  3   plastic containers
  1   colored marker

Management Tip: Students will record their observations, ideas, and questions in their science notebooks each day. In some lessons, students also will use record sheets, which they will store in their notebooks. Teachers have found that a folder with pockets and fasteners for loose-leaf paper works best for storing the record sheets. Students may use a spiral notebook if they create a pocket on the inside of one cover.

Preparation

1. Review this lesson as it is presented in the Student Activity Book. Decide when you want to distribute the books to the students.

2. Label two sheets of newsprint with the words "What We Know about Rocks." Put the date on each sheet. Label the other two sheets "What We Want to Know about Rocks." Have extra sheets available.

3. Make a copy of **Record Sheet 1-A: Rocks—Record of My Observations** for each student.

4. Create a classroom materials center for distribution and storage of the rocks and other supplies. Place the three numbered rocks in separate plastic containers that have been labeled 1, 2, or 3. Figure 1-1 shows one way to set up a materials center.

Figure 1-1

Materials center

5. Decide on a process for distributing and collecting materials. Each pair of students should be responsible for storing their own materials at the end of the lesson.

6. Assign each student a partner. The language skills of the members of each pair should be complementary.

Procedure

1. Distribute a science notebook to each student. Ask students to write their names and the current date on the first sheet. Explain that they will record data and observations in their notebooks daily. Emphasize the importance of dating every entry.

2. To introduce the unit, ask students to think for a minute about rocks. Use the following questions to focus their thoughts:

   ■ What do you know about rocks?

   ■ Where have you found rocks?

   ■ How are rocks used?

3. Ask students to write their thoughts on the dated page in their science notebooks.

4. Have students share their ideas about rocks. Record their comments on the class list entitled "What We Know about Rocks."

5. Ask students if they have any questions about rocks. Record their questions on the class list entitled "What We Want to Know about Rocks." Figure 1-2 illustrates some responses of other third-graders. Hang both class lists prominently in the room.

Management Tip: You will add new ideas and questions to both class lists throughout the unit. The lists also will be used as a basis of comparison in the post-unit assessment. Use a different-colored marker for each addition, and record its date.

Figure 1-2

Sample student responses

6. Show a sample set of rocks 1, 2, and 3 to the class. Let students know that they will now observe and describe these rocks.

7. Ask one student from each pair to go to the materials center to collect the following:

    ■ 1 set of rocks 1, 2, and 3

    ■ 1 cardboard tray

    ■ 2 hand lenses

8. Encourage students to explore with the hand lens by examining the writing in their notebooks, their fingernails, a pencil, or any other nearby object. Check to make sure that all the students can see the objects clearly. It is usually easiest for students of this age to hold the object still and slowly move the hand lens back and forth above it until the object comes into focus. Scientists usually put the lens within 3 cm of the eye and then move the object to bring it into focus.

9. Let students spend about five minutes exploring the rocks. Encourage them to share observations with their partners.

Figure 1-3

*Exploring with
a hand lens*

Figure 1-4

*Third-graders'
observations
about rocks*

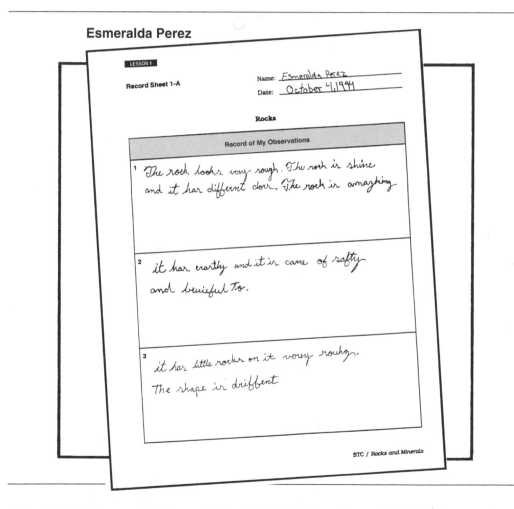

10. Distribute a copy of **Record Sheet 1-A: Rocks—Record of My Observations** to each student. Ask students to record as many observations as possible for each rock. When they have finished, remind them to place the record sheet in the pocket of their notebooks. Figures 1-4 and 1-5 show some samples of third-grade students' observations about rocks.

11. Ask students to return the rocks, trays, and hand lenses to the materials center. Have them return each rock to the appropriately numbered plastic container.

Figure 1-5

*Sample student
notebook entries*

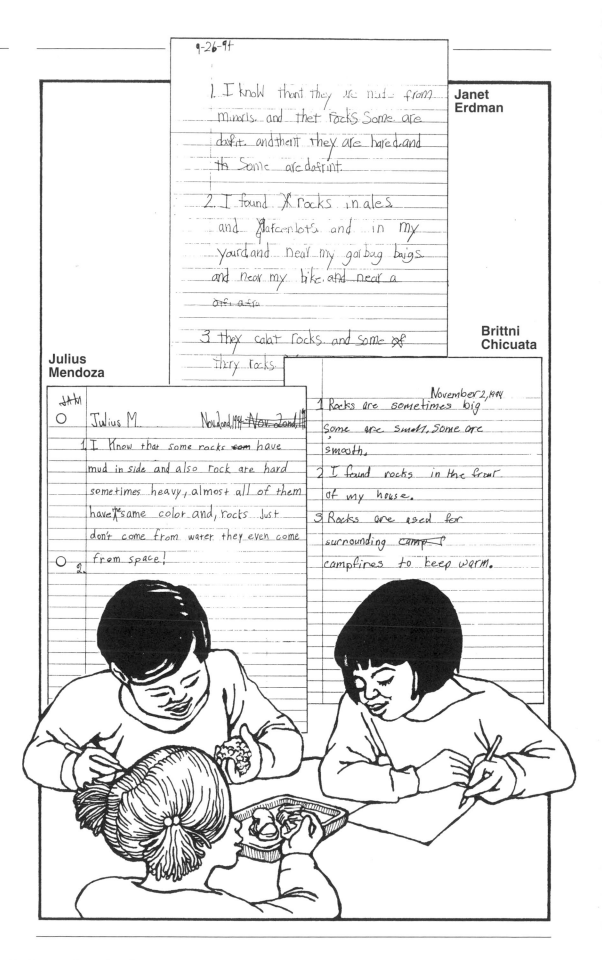

**Janet
Erdman**

9-26-94

1. I know thant they are nut from minorls. and thet rocks Some are dafit. andthent they are hared.and th Some are dofrint.

2. I found X rocks in ales and gafcenlots. and in my yourd.and near my gorbug baigs and near my bike.and near a ori. afra

3 they calat rocks. and some of Thry rocks.

**Julius
Mendoza**

JAM
O Julius M.   Nov.2and/1994 Nov.2and/994

1 I know that some rocks com have mud in side and also rock are hard sometimes heavy, almost all of them have the same color and, rocks Just don't come from water they even come
O from space!
  2.

**Brittni
Chicuata**

November 2, 1994

1 Rocks are sometimes big Some are small, Some are smooth.

2 I found rocks in the front of my house.

3 Rocks are used for surrounding camf campfires to keep werm.

Final Activities

1. Ask students to think about rock 1. Was it heavy or light? Bumpy or smooth? Let students know that words like these describe the rock's properties. Properties are the individual features of rocks. Now ask students to name some properties that they observed and recorded for rocks 2 and 3.

2. Help students summarize their observations with questions such as the following:

   ■ What properties are the same for all three rocks?

   ■ What properties are different for each of the three rocks?

3. Ask students to write in their science notebooks the words they used to describe the propertics of rocks.

Extensions

SCIENCE

1. Create a rock learning center. Ask students to bring in rocks they have found. Encourage other students to examine the rocks with a hand lens.

LANGUAGE ARTS

2. Ask each student to describe what he or she has learned about rocks today to a friend or someone at home and then to request the listener to write down a question about rocks. Ask the student to bring the question to school and share it with the class. Create a class list of questions and place a check mark by each question as it is answered.

LANGUAGE ARTS

3. Create an adjective chart on which students can record words that describe rocks. Encourage students to add to the chart throughout the upcoming lessons.

Assessment

In the section Teaching *Rocks and Minerals* (pgs. 6–12), you will find a detailed discussion about the assessment of students' learning. The specific goals and related assessments for this unit are summarized in Figure T-1 on pgs. 9–10.

Students' writing in their science notebooks and the ideas they suggest during the class brainstorming session provide a baseline of their knowledge of rocks and their ideas about them. In Lesson 5, they will provide similar baseline information about minerals. You will ask students the questions from both lessons again as part of the post-unit assessment. By comparing responses from the pre- and post-unit assessments, you will be able to document both individual and class learning. Ideas to note today and at the end of the unit include:

■ Are students aware that rocks and minerals are not the same?

■ What information do students have about rocks?

■ What do students know about how rocks are used?

■ Have students studied rocks previously, either in school or elsewhere?

■ Do students understand what a property is?

Observations that students have entered on **Record Sheet 1-A** will indicate their baseline skills in observing and describing. Specific skills to note today include:

■ How detailed are students' oral descriptions of their observations?

■ What properties, other than size, do students describe?

■ What comparisons do students make?

■ How detailed are students' written descriptions?

Record Sheet 1–A

Name: _____

Date: _____

Rocks

Record of My Observations
1
2
3

Observing Rocks: How Are They the Same and Different?

Overview and Objectives

Building on their observations in Lesson 1, students now explore nine additional rocks to discover more about the diversity among rocks. Through class discussions of properties, students begin to recognize that they can describe a rock in many different ways. After sorting their rocks on the basis of a property of their own choice, students expand their observational skills by sorting the 12 rocks on the basis of properties suggested by their classmates. Students will apply these experiences in Lesson 3, when they are introduced to one way in which geologists describe and classify rocks.

- Students observe and describe the properties of 12 rocks.

- Students sort rocks according to similarities and differences they observe.

- Students describe and discuss the properties that were the basis of each sort.

- Students sort rocks according to properties suggested by their classmates.

Background

The 12 rocks in this unit were chosen because they are common, provide a range of observable properties (including color, texture, and layering), and have a number of common uses.

Information about each of the rocks that students will explore in this unit is presented in alphabetical order in the Rock Information Cards at the end of Lesson 16 (pgs. 132–37). Names of the rocks appear in the **Preparation** section of this lesson. Although naming each rock is not a goal in this unit, your students may ask for the name of some rocks whose properties they find particularly interesting. When the properties of a rock capture their interest, students are more likely to connect that rock with its name.

The students' first step in learning about their rocks is free exploration, which gives them an opportunity to focus on the properties that capture their interest. The second step, sorting, provides a way for students to find out more about the physical properties of each of the rocks. As the students sort the rocks, exchange information, and describe the rocks' properties, they begin to appreciate the diversity inherent in rocks. Later in the unit, students will learn about the relationship between the properties and uses of rocks.

Management Tip: Students may start bringing in rocks they have found. Create a display area in the classroom where they can explore each other's rocks. Encourage students to use adjectives from the list they created in Lesson 1 to describe properties that can be used as a basis for sorting the rocks.

Materials

For each student
  1 science notebook
  1 copy of **Record Sheet 1-A: Rocks—Record of My Observations** (from Lesson 1)
  1 hand lens

For every two students
  1 set of 12 rocks, labeled 1–12
  1 cardboard tray

For the class
  12 plastic containers
      Class lists "What We Know about Rocks" and "What We Want to Know about Rocks" (from Lesson 1)

Preparation

1. Post the two class lists from Lesson 1.

2. Examine the 12 rocks to familiarize yourself with their observable properties. The names of the rocks are as follows:

1.	Granite	7.	Obsidian
2.	Gneiss	8.	Basalt
3.	Conglomerate	9.	Pumice
4.	Limestone	10.	Slate
5.	Shale	11.	Marble
6.	Sandstone	12.	Schist

    You will find additional information about each of the rocks at the end of Lesson 16 (pgs. 132–37).

3. Set up the materials center. A suggested arrangement is shown in Figure 2-1.

4. Decide on a process for distributing and collecting the materials.

Procedure

1. Encourage students to review **Record Sheet 1-A: Rocks—Record of My Observations.** Ask them to think of one property of each of the rocks they studied in Lesson 1.

2. Let the students know that during the next three lessons, they will explore a collection of 12 rocks: the 3 rocks from Lesson 1 and 9 new ones.

3. Ask students to think of their senses. How many senses are there? How could they use their senses to gain information about the rocks?

Safety Note: Remind students that although the sense of taste might provide interesting or useful information, it is never used in science class.

---

4. Ask that one student from each pair pick up 12 different rocks, a cardboard tray, and two hand lenses from the materials center.

5. Give students time to explore the rocks using all their senses except taste. Encourage them to describe the rocks to each other as they explore.

Figure 2-1

Materials center

Figure 2-2

Sorting the
12 rocks

6. Ask the students to sort their rocks according to similarities and differences they observe.

7. Invite a student to describe how he or she sorted the rocks. List the property on the board and challenge the other students to sort their rocks according to that property. Compare and discuss results. If necessary, help the student clarify his or her description of the property. (Properties that students are most likely to suggest are size, color, weight, layering, and presence of fossils.)

8. Ask other students, one by one, to share additional properties and list them on the board. Again, have students sort their rocks and discuss results.

9. Ask students to return their supplies to the materials center.

Final Activities

1. Ask students to think about one property that was shared during the class discussion. Have them write several sentences about that property in their science notebooks. Use the following questions to help students focus on the task:

   ■ What property did you choose?

   ■ Did you describe a property to the class? If so, what words did you use?

   ■ After you sorted your rocks by that property, how many groups did you have?

2. Refer to the class lists "What We Know about Rocks" and "What We Want to Know about Rocks." Ask students whether they have any ideas or questions to add to these lists. If so, write them on the appropriate list. Be sure to use a different-colored marker and to add the date.

Extensions

MATHEMATICS   ART

1. Ask students whether they have ever found a fossil. If so, ask them to draw a picture of it. As a class, decide how to sort the pictures. Then create a class picture graph. Let students write number sentences to compare how many fossils of each type were found.

LANGUAGE ARTS

2. Encourage students to read about fossils and to share what they learn with the class. Refer to the Bibliography (pgs. 151–54) for resources. Your school librarian should also be able to suggest appropriate books.

SOCIAL STUDIES

3. "Pet rocks" were popular in the 1970s. Have students interview adults in their families about this fad. Did any of them have a pet rock? If so, what did they find appealing about them?

LANGUAGE ARTS

4. Arrange a center where students can make their own pet rocks. Then encourage them to write a story describing what makes their rock a good "pet."

Learning More about Rocks

Overview and Objectives

Students have now observed and described the physical properties of 12 rocks. In the reading selection in this lesson, they are introduced to two key concepts. The first is that rocks are formed in different ways; the second, that rocks are continually changing. The reading selection also introduces students to an approach that geologists use to classify rocks. As they observe the differences among rocks that were formed in a similar way, students start to understand the complex process of rock formation. As they note the similarities among rocks formed from other rocks, students gain an appreciation of the concept that rocks are constantly changing.

- Students use a Venn diagram to identify and discuss similarities and differences among rocks.

- Students read about and discuss how rocks are formed.

- Students identify observable properties that are related to how rocks are formed.

- Students use properties related to how rocks are formed to sort rocks by classes: sedimentary, igneous, or metamorphic.

Background

The field of geology has many different branches, each of which has a different focus. For example, some geologists concentrate on increasing our knowledge and understanding of rocks and minerals and the relation between them. Other geologists, including geophysical and mining engineers, are concerned with finding mineral resources and determining how they can most efficiently be removed from the earth.

Geologists who specialize in the various branches of their science have different ways of grouping rocks. For example, those who are interested in historical geology group rocks on the basis of how they were formed. They use three broad, and sometimes overlapping, categories: sedimentary, igneous, and metamorphic. Each of the categories has subdivisions.

Rocks are continually changing and forming new rocks. Sometimes this happens as a result of weathering. Wind, rain, ice, and snow break down rocks. Rocks also change as the result of heat or pressure. This heat or pressure can be violent and dramatic, as in volcanic eruptions and earthquakes. At other times, the changes produced by heat and pressure occur deep beneath the surface of the earth and are slower and subtler. The interrelated processes by which rocks change and form new rocks is called the **rock cycle.**

Sedimentary rocks form from layered particles of weathered rocks and minerals. As these particles are deposited and buried under other accumulating materials, they become compacted. Many sedimentary rocks are relatively soft. Sedimentary rocks often have distinct horizontal layers. Fossils may be found in sedimentary rocks such as limestone, shale, and sandstone.

Some **igneous rocks** are formed from **magma,** which is molten rock underground. Igneous rocks that are formed underground tend to be coarse-grained. They are sometimes called **intrusive** (where the magma has entered cracks or forced apart other rocks) or **plutonic** rocks. Other igneous rocks are formed from lava during volcanic eruptions. These rocks, which are called **extrusive,** are fine-grained and can be very smooth.

Igneous rocks often have distinct mineral crystals. The size of the crystals depends on how quickly the molten rock has cooled. If it cooled slowly, the crystals tend to be large; if it cooled quickly, the crystals are small. Igneous rocks tend to be harder than sedimentary rocks, and they usually do not display layering.

Solid rock that has been changed as a result of heat, pressure, or reaction with water is called **metamorphic rock.** These powerful forces can twist or distort the layers in sedimentary rocks. Re-formed crystals can sometimes be seen in metamorphic rocks.

Some rocks display distinctive, observable properties that relate to the way they were formed. For example, obsidian (sometimes called "volcanic glass") is black and shiny. It forms when lava rapidly cools and then hardens upon being spewed into the air from an erupting volcano. In other cases, appearance is not a conclusive indicator of how a rock was formed. Slate and shale, for example, look quite similar, yet they were formed in different ways. In fact, slate is formed from shale!

The intent of this lesson is to help students begin to connect their observations of some of the rocks with the processes by which they were formed. The information in this lesson will provide students with a base of information that will be helpful in the upper grades, when they study the rock cycle in greater detail. As students read the story and sort rocks, remind them to look for properties. Reassure them that even geologists cannot always identify a rock just by looking at it.

Materials

For each student
  1 science notebook
  1 hand lens

For every two students
  1 set of rocks, labeled 1–12
  1 cardboard tray

For the class
    Class lists "What We Know about Rocks" and "What We Want to Know about Rocks" (from Lesson 1)
  1 colored marker

Preparation

1. Read "Rocks—Here, There, Everywhere" on pgs. 35–36 of the Teacher's Guide (pgs. 11–12 of the Student Activity Book). Compare the 12 rock samples with the descriptions in the reading selection.

2. Post the class lists from Lesson 1.

3. Prepare the containers of rocks, cardboard trays, and hand lenses for distribution.

Procedure

1. Ask students to review what they wrote in their notebooks during Lesson 2. Then pose the following questions:

   ■ What properties did you use to sort the rocks?

   ■ Were there any rocks that could have gone into more than one group?

   ■ Were there any rocks that did not appear to fit into any of your groups?

2. Ask one student from each pair to collect the 12 different rocks, a cardboard tray, and two hand lenses from the materials center.

3. Ask the students to look at their rocks as they discuss how the rocks are different and how they are the same. Encourage them to consider the following questions:

   ■ How do the rocks feel?

   ■ How do they look?

   ■ Which rocks are heavy? Which ones are light?

   ■ How are they all alike? How are they all different?

4. Have students turn to "Rocks—Here, There, Everywhere" on pgs. 11–12 in the Student Activity Book. Read the selection, either as a class or in pairs. After the students have read each section, stop and let them explore the rocks again.

5. Have one student from each pair return the rocks, cardboard trays, and hand lenses to the materials center.

Figure 3-1

Reading about rocks

Final Activities

1. Ask students to write in their science notebooks any new ideas they now have about rocks. Also ask them to record any new questions they have about rocks.

2. Invite students to share the ideas they wrote in their notebooks.

3. Referring to the class list entitled "What We Know about Rocks," compare students' current ideas with those they had in Lesson 1. With a different-colored marker, add new ideas. Draw a line through ideas students now know are not correct.

4. Review the questions on the class list entitled "What We Would Like to Know about Rocks." With a different-colored marker, place a check by the questions that have been answered. Add students' new questions to the list.

Extensions

LANGUAGE ARTS

1. Have students interview their parents or other adults who remember the eruption of Mount St. Helens. Students may also want to research and report on how wildlife and vegetation have returned to the area since the devastation caused by the volcanic eruption.

LANGUAGE ARTS

2. Read a book about volcanoes, such as *Volcano*, by Patricia Lauber, to the class (see Bibliography).

SCIENCE

3. Invite a geologist to share additional rock samples with the class. Suggest that the geologist bring in a sample of volcanic ash, if possible.

Reading Selection

Rocks—Here, There, Everywhere

You can find rocks just about anywhere. One rock can be very different from another. Remember the properties you and your partner described when you looked at your rocks? Did you know that the properties of a rock can give you clues about how it was formed?

Rocks Formed under Water

Have you ever seen a rock with layers? Some of these rocks were formed under water. They are made up of pieces of other rocks and things like sand, clay, and mud that settled in layers under water. After a long time, the layers piled up and stuck together.

Sometimes, plants, bones, or sea shells got caught in the layers. They formed fossils. Some **fossils** are the prints of plants and animals that lived long ago. Other fossils are actual parts of plants or animals that have been mineralized. Can you find fossils in any of your rocks?

Do you know what a pebble is? If you look closely, you can see pebbles in some rocks that formed under water.

Because these rocks are formed of **sediment,** or bits and pieces of matter that have settled to the bottom of water, scientists call them **sedimentary** rocks.

Look at your rocks. Which ones might be sedimentary? Why?

Rocks Formed under Ground

Some rocks were formed inside the earth. Deep inside the earth, it is very hot. In fact, it is so hot that rocks melt! Melted underground rock is called **magma.**

sedimentary -3, 4, 5, 6
igneous - 1, 7, 8, 9,
metamorphic - 2, 10, 11, 12

Sometimes the magma erupts through the surface of the earth. Rocks, flames, and steam spout toward the sky. When this happens, the magma gets a new name. It is called **lava.** As the lava piles up and hardens, it forms a volcano.

Rocks from volcanoes don't always look the same. Some look like glass. They are smooth. This is because they cooled fast. Other rocks from volcanoes cooled slowly. Gas bubbled out, causing small holes to form. Their surface is often rough.

Volcanoes often erupt more than once. As soon as the lava starts to harden, more lava lands on top of it! Rocks formed this way have bands, or streaks, in them.

Sometimes the magma cools very slowly underground. Rocks formed in this way are very hard and heavy. You can see pieces of minerals in them.

Rocks formed from magma are called **igneous.** Which of your rocks do you think could be igneous? What properties make you think so?

Changed Rocks

Rocks don't always stay where they are formed. Over time, earthquakes move them around. As rocks are moved, they can change. They become twisted. They can even break up.

Think about tearing a piece of a paper. It's easy, isn't it? But could you tear up a telephone book? You'd have to be pretty strong. And do you think anyone could be strong enough to tear up a rock? Probably not. But rocks can tear as a result of underground pressure.

Heat also changes rocks. There is heat just under the surface of the earth. It is not hot enough to turn rocks into liquid, but it is hot enough to change them. Think about what happens to a grilled cheese sandwich. The cheese is solid at first, but as soon as it heats up, it becomes soft. It changes form. The same thing can happen to rocks.

Find rocks 5 and 10. Rock 10 was formed from a rock like 5. How are they alike? How are they different? Rocks that have been changed by underground pressure or heat are called **metamorphic.**

Which other rocks do you think could be metamorphic? What properties make you think so?

Rocks will give us clues about how and where they were formed—if we take time to look at them closely.

Discovering Minerals

Overview and Objectives

After reviewing what they now know about rocks, students begin to investigate minerals. As students compare their 12 rocks with 3 minerals, focusing on the similarities and differences between them, they explore the concept that rocks contain minerals. Students also have the opportunity to refine their skills in observing, describing, and recording properties. These activities, coupled with those in Lesson 5, prepare students for Lesson 6, where they begin to assemble the data that they will use to create their "Minerals Field Guide." Students will revisit the concept that rocks contain minerals at the end of the unit.

- Students review and summarize the properties of the rocks they have observed.

- Students compare rocks and minerals and discuss the similarities and differences between them.

- Students observe and describe three minerals.

- Students record and discuss their observations of three minerals.

Background

Minerals are naturally occurring, solid substances with distinct physical and chemical properties. Different samples of the same mineral sometimes look very different from one another; however, the chemical composition of a given mineral is always the same. That composition, moreover, is consistent throughout the entire mineral. For this reason, geologists often classify minerals on the basis of their chemical composition. The composition of various samples of the same rock, by contrast, is not consistent.

Isolated mineral specimens are rarely found on the surface of the earth. As noted in Lesson 1, most minerals are found in rocks. The mineral grains in some rocks can be observed with the unaided eye or a hand lens. In other cases, minerals can be identified only with a microscope, a chemical test, special X-ray equipment, or a scanning electron microscope.

Geologists classify minerals on the basis of similarities in their internal (atomic) structure. In this lesson, students will examine three minerals: feldspar, quartz, and galena. **Feldspar** and **quartz** are members of the **silicate group.** All silicates contain silica and oxygen; they may also contain other minerals such as aluminum and sodium. **Galena** is a member of the **sulfide** group. The key element of sulfides is sulfur.

Feldspar is the most common mineral on earth. Many clays are weathered forms of feldspar. Feldspar often appears as very small crystals in a rock. However, some of the largest individual crystals are also feldspar—they can weigh more than 2,000 tons. Feldspar can be pink, white, or gray. It is a component of most igneous, many metamorphic, and some sedimentary rocks.

Quartz is frequently found in surface rocks. Quartz is resistant to weathering, and small particles of it are commonly found in sedimentary rocks. Quartz is often the predominant mineral in sand.

Quartz is found in a variety of forms. The sample students will examine in this lesson is a single, large crystal. Other forms of quartz that display crystals are named on the basis of their color and include amethyst, citrine, and smoky quartz. The rose quartz used later in this unit and most samples of milky quartz are called **massive;** in other words, they are formed of a mass of crystals.

Some quartz specimens are composed of crystals so small that they are visible only under a microscope. As a result, they are called **microcrystalline.** Examples of these forms of quartz include jasper, chert (flint), and onyx.

Galena is a major source of lead. It is sometimes found with silver. Galena is found in a range of igneous, metamorphic, and sedimentary rocks. It has a cubic shape and a metallic luster. (See the box below for important information on handling galena.)

Safety Rules for Handling Galena

Galena is a form of lead sulfide, a compound that commonly occurs in the earth's crust. An attractive mineral with interesting physical properties, galena is widely used in earth science classes.

The Environmental Health Center of the National Safety Council notes that lead is poisonous in all forms and that lead poisoning is cumulative. Lead sulfide, however, is less toxic than the more soluble lead compounds, such as lead acetate, lead chloride, and lead oxide. (National Safety Council's Environmental Writer Chemical Backgrounder Web site: http://www.nsc.org/ehc/ew/chems/leadcmp2.htm). The National Center for Environmental Health at the Centers for Disease Control and Prevention in Atlanta has indicated that skin contact with galena is not dangerous. Nonetheless, to avoid any potential ingestion, people should always wash their hands after handling galena.

We recommend that teachers take the following safety precautions when using the galena samples in the STC™ *Rocks and Minerals* kit:

- Inform students that galena, like all compounds containing lead, is poisonous if it is taken internally.

- To reduce the risk of ingestion by hand-to-mouth contact, have students wear disposable plastic gloves when they handle galena.

- Tell students to wash their hands after handling galena.

- Allow students access to the galena samples only under direct supervision.

- Do not allow students to take galena samples out of the classroom.

Materials

For each student
1 science notebook
1 **Record Sheet 4-A: Minerals—Record of My Observations**
1 **Record Sheet 1-A: Rocks—Record of My Observations** (from Lesson 1)
1 hand lens
1 pair of disposable gloves

For every two students
1 set of 12 rocks, labeled 1–12
1 set of 3 minerals, labeled A–C
1 cardboard tray

For the class
1 sheet of newsprint, 60 × 90 cm (24 × 36 in)
2 colored markers
1 pad of Post-it® notes, 76 × 127 mm (3 × 5 in)
3 additional plastic containers (for minerals A, B, and C)

Preparation

1. Draw a large circle on a sheet of newsprint and label it "Rocks." This will be one of two circles in a Venn diagram that students will use to compare rocks and minerals. During this lesson, you will record students' ideas about rocks on Post-it® notes and place the notes inside the circle. You will create the "Minerals" circle in Lesson 13. In Lesson 16, you will overlap the two circles to complete the Venn diagram, which will show the similarities and differences between rocks and minerals. For more information on Venn diagrams, please turn to pg. 7.

2. Wearing a pair of disposable gloves, examine the three minerals to become familiar with their properties. The names of the minerals are feldspar (A), quartz (B), and galena (C).

3. Label three of the plastic containers with the letters A, B, and C. Place minerals A to C in them. Set up the materials center with the 12 rocks and 3 minerals in their plastic containers, a cardboard tray for each pair of students, the disposable gloves, and hand lenses.

4. Make a copy of **Record Sheet 4-A: Minerals—Record of My Observations** for each student.

Procedure

1. Ask the students to review the information they have recorded about rocks on **Record Sheet 1-A: Rocks—Record of My Observations** and in their science notebooks.

2. Ask students to suggest properties shared by all the rocks. Record their ideas on the Post-it® notes. Place the notes inside the circle labeled "Rocks," as shown in Figure 4-1.

3. Have one student from each pair put on a pair of disposable gloves and pick up the 12 rocks and 3 minerals, a cardboard tray, another pair of disposable gloves, and two hand lenses from the materials center.

Figure 4-1

The first circle for the class Venn diagram

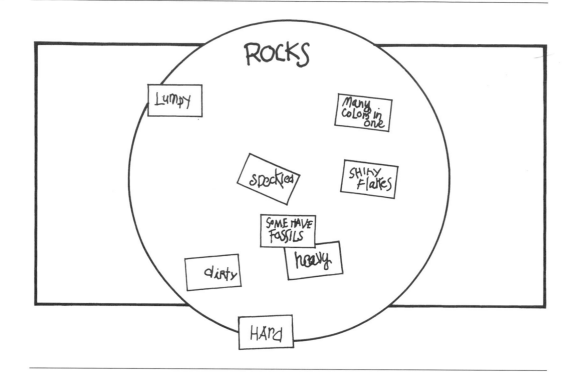

4. Let the students know that the three new objects are minerals and that they will be exploring minerals for the next few weeks. Instruct students to put on their disposable gloves before handling any of the minerals. Ask them to observe the minerals and compare them with the rocks. How are they similar? How are they different?

5. Distribute **Record Sheet 4-A: Minerals—Record of My Observations.** Ask students to record their observations about the minerals.

6. Ask students to use their hand lenses to examine the rocks. Use the following questions to focus their observations:

   ■ Which rocks have tiny pieces in them?

   ■ What do you think they are?

Figure 4-2

Magnification can reveal minerals in a rock

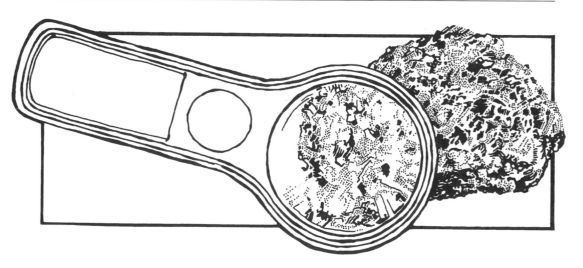

- Do any of the minerals look like these pieces?

- Which rocks look like they might have little pieces of mineral A in them? Mineral B? Mineral C?

7. Have students return their supplies to the materials center, throw away their gloves, and wash their hands. Instruct students that the proper way to take off their gloves is by holding on to the gloves at the wrist opening and pulling the glove up over their fingers. This turns the glove inside out as it is pulled off.

Figure 4-3

Third-graders' observations about minerals

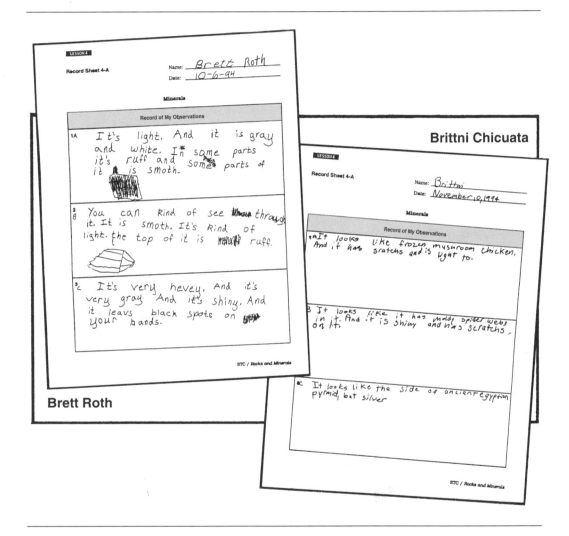

Brett Roth

Brittni Chicuata

Final Activities

1. Ask students to review **Record Sheet 4-A** and to share their descriptions of each mineral. Figure 4-3 shows samples of third-graders' recorded observations about minerals.

2. Ask students to think about how rocks and minerals are similar and different. Ask them to record their thoughts in their notebooks.

Management Tip: You may temporarily put the rocks away after this lesson. Students will not use them again until Lesson 16.

Extensions

> **SCIENCE**

1. Invite students to bring in additional rocks to add to the learning center.

> **SCIENCE** **LANGUAGE ARTS**

2. Arrange a field trip to a rock shop or museum. Challenge students to find samples of the same rock that look different. Have them record the name of the rock and list its differences and similarities.

> **SOCIAL STUDIES** **MATHEMATICS**

3. Engage students in a traditional math logic game that uses rocks. Examples are Barngara or Move Move, which is from the Solomon Islands.

Assessment

This lesson provides an opportunity to assess the degree to which your students' ability to observe and describe rocks has grown over the past three lessons. As you are reading their notebook entries and record sheets, examining the properties they suggest for the Venn diagram, and listening to their comments, look for the following:

- Use of language that describes the property they have observed in a manner that their classmates understand

- Descriptive words and phrases that would help a listener or reader differentiate among several rocks

- Comparisons among a group of rocks (for example, "Rock 1 is heavier than rocks 4 and 7, but lighter than rocks 5 and 9.")

- Attention to and application of information from other students

- Review, interpretation, and application of information recorded in previous lessons to new situations

Note: Some of your students may be starting to use specialized vocabulary when naming and describing rocks and rock categories. Others may not yet be ready to use such terms with understanding. The use of specialized terms is not emphasized in this unit, and it should not be used as the only indicator of students' understanding. More useful indicators are growth in students' ability to sort, classify, describe, and compare rocks and minerals.

Record Sheet 4–A

Name: _____

Date: _____

Minerals

Record of My Observations
A
B
C

Sharing What We Know about Minerals

Overview and Objectives

This lesson continues the students' introduction to minerals. It also serves as a pre-unit assessment of their knowledge of and questions about minerals. Using the 3 minerals from the previous lesson and 9 new ones, students explore two concepts—the similarities in physical properties between two samples of a single mineral and the differences among the 12 minerals. During the next eight lessons, students will expand their understanding of minerals as they observe, describe, and record the physical and chemical properties of their 12 samples. Students will apply this information in Lesson 14, when they identify the minerals by name by comparing the data they have collected with information provided by a geologist.

■ Students share their ideas and questions about minerals.

■ Students observe and describe 12 minerals.

■ Students compare and discuss their observations of the 12 minerals.

■ Students compare and describe similarities between samples of the same mineral.

Background

More than 3,500 minerals have been found in the earth's crust. Given this diversity, how do geologists identify a mineral? Identification is possible because each mineral has distinctive physical and chemical properties that vary only within narrow limits. Physical properties include hardness, luster, color, cleavage (the way it splits), fracture (the way it breaks), and specific gravity (its relative density). The chemical properties of a mineral are related to its atomic structure and chemical composition.

Minerals can sometimes be identified on the basis of physical properties alone by using nothing more than careful observation and a simple hand lens. This may be possible, for example, if the mineral sample is pure or if its properties are extremely distinctive. But minerals are usually found embedded in rocks; in this case, identification on the basis of physical properties alone can be more difficult. In addition, two or more minerals may share certain physical properties.

In such cases, geologists use sophisticated techniques, including chemical tests, to identify the mineral. With methods that involve electron microscopy, X-rays, and chemical analysis, geologists have gained new understanding of the atomic structure and chemical composition of minerals. In fact, they are reclassifying minerals whose properties had not been fully understood.

Geologists recognize that certain minerals are sufficiently similar to be grouped together in families. Orthoclase and plagioclase, for example, are members of the feldspar family. The quartz family includes amethyst, citrine, and jasper. The mica family includes biotite and muscovite.

After they examine their 12 minerals, students read about feldspar, one of the minerals in their set. They will read about one or two minerals at the end of each of the next seven lessons. Again, remember that knowing the names of the minerals is not the focus of these activities. In Lesson 14, students are challenged to apply all the information they have gathered to help them identify each mineral by name.

Materials

For each student

  1   science notebook

  1   **Record Sheet 4-A: Minerals—Record of My Observations** (from Lesson 4)

  1   hand lens

  1   pair of disposable gloves

For every two students

  1   set of 12 minerals, labeled A–L

  1   egg carton

  1   cardboard tray

  1   colored marker

For the class

  4   sheets of newsprint, 60 × 90 cm (24 × 36 in)

 12   plastic containers

Preparation

1. Label two sheets of newsprint "What We Know about Minerals" and two sheets "What We Want to Know about Minerals." Post both sheets prominently in the room.

Management Tip: Keep the two class lists on display throughout the rest of the unit. Add new ideas and questions as they arise. As a question is answered, put a check by it. The lists will also be used for comparison in the post-unit assessment.

2. Wearing gloves, examine several samples of each of the 12 minerals. Note the similarities and differences among samples of a single mineral and of the different minerals. The names of the minerals are as follows:

A. Feldspar	G. Hematite
B. Quartz	H. Gypsum
C. Galena	I. Magnetite
D. Calcite	J. Muscovite
E. Fluorite	K. Sulfur
F. Graphite	L. Talc

3. Label nine additional plastic containers, place the nine new minerals in them, and add them to the materials center, along with the other minerals, hand lenses, disposable gloves, and cardboard trays. Place the 15 markers and egg cartons aside. You will distribute them during Step 7 of the **Procedure** section.

Management Tip: Near the end of this lesson, each pair of students will arrange a set of 12 minerals in an egg carton. The students will write their names on the lid of the carton. Each student pair will use the same set of minerals throughout the remainder of the unit, returning it to the materials center at the end of each lesson.

Figure 5-1

Labeled egg carton

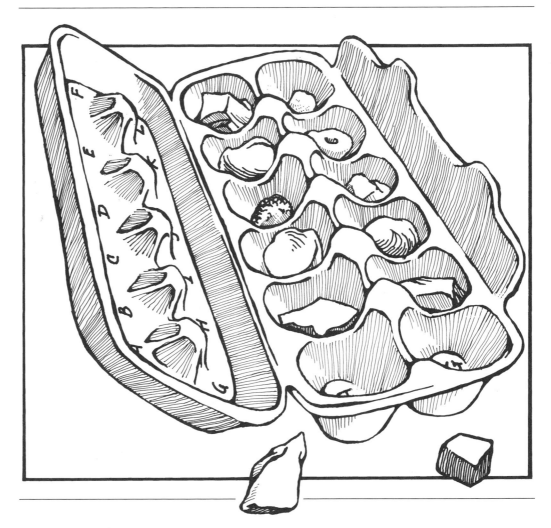

4. Label the 12 sections of an egg carton A to L. Place a set of the labeled minerals in the corresponding sections. Students will use this carton as a reference in preparing and checking their own mineral collections.

5. Read the information about feldspar on pg. 53 of this guide.

Procedure

1. Referring to the two sheets of prepared newsprint, ask students to think about what they know about minerals and what questions they have about them. Have them record their thoughts in their science notebooks. Focus their thinking with questions such as the following:

   ■ What do you know about minerals?

   ■ Where have you seen minerals?

   ■ How are minerals used?

2. Invite students to share their ideas about minerals. Record these on the class list entitled "What We Know about Minerals."

3. Now ask students to share their questions about minerals. Record these on the class list entitled "What We Want to Know about Minerals." Responses from other third-grade students appear in Figure 5-2.

Figure 5-2

Sample student questions

4. Ask one student from each pair to put on a pair of disposable gloves and pick up the following materials:

   ▪ 1 sample of each of the 12 minerals

   ▪ 1 cardboard tray

   ▪ 2 hand lenses

   ▪ 1 pair of disposable gloves

5. Remind students to put on their gloves. (In the upcoming lessons in this unit, continue reminding students to put on their gloves before they handle the minerals.) Then ask the students to spend 5 to 10 minutes with their partners describing, comparing, and sorting the minerals.

6. Challenge students to answer the following questions as they compare their sample of a certain mineral with the sample of another pair of students:

   ■ How are both samples of the same mineral alike?

   ■ Do you see any differences between the samples?

   ■ Do you think you both have the same mineral? Why or why not?

7. Give each pair of students an egg carton and a colored marker. Show them your labeled carton. Have them label the sections of their cartons in the same way. Have each member of the pair write his or her name on the lid of the carton. Let students know that they should return each mineral to its appropriate place at the end of every class.

8. Ask students to return their cartons of minerals and other supplies to the materials center and to throw away their gloves. Remind them also to wash their hands. Collect the markers.

Figure 5-3

Labeling the mineral cartons

Final Activities

1. Ask students to think about the following questions and write their thoughts in their science notebooks:

   ■ Have you ever seen minerals like these? Where?

   ■ How are these minerals different from others you have seen?

   ■ How are they similar?

2. Ask students to discuss their observations. Were these minerals similar to ones they have seen before?

3. As a class or in pairs, read the information about feldspar on pg. 17 of the Student Activity Book (pg. 53 of the Teacher's Guide).

Extensions

LANGUAGE ARTS

1. Create an adjective chart for minerals. Encourage students to add new adjectives over the next few weeks. Have them refer to the chart when deciding how to describe their observations.

LANGUAGE ARTS

2. Read a book about a geologist to the class. One possibility is *Susan Humphris, Geologist,* by Liza Ketchum Murrow (see Bibliography).

Assessment

Students' responses during the brainstorming session and in their science notebooks provide baseline indicators of their knowledge of and ideas about minerals. This information complements the pre-unit assessment of students' knowledge of rocks, which appeared in Lesson 1. Following Lesson 16, you will ask these same questions as a post-unit assessment. By comparing responses, you will gain insight into students' learning and be able to document their progress.

Reading Selection

Feldspar

Feldspar is the German word for "field mineral." Feldspar is the most common mineral in the earth's crust. You can find feldspar almost anywhere in the world. You can see small pieces of it in the sand at the beach. Feldspar is also found in rocks. Some igneous rocks are made almost entirely of feldspar.

Sometimes feldspar is white. A beautiful and very rare gem, called the moonstone, is white feldspar. Feldspar can also be pink, green, or red. Geologists use names like "orthoclase," "microcline," and "plagioclase" to describe these different types of feldspar. You might say that all these minerals are members of the feldspar group or "family." Orthoclase and plagioclase are a source of clay that is used to make dishes and pottery. The clay forms slowly from feldspar during weathering.

Much of the world's best orthoclase is found in England. Kaolin, which comes from a weathered feldspar, is also used in a medicine called Kaopectate™. Have you ever been given Kaopectate™?

Observing Minerals: How Are They the Same and Different?

Overview and Objectives

In this lesson, students' explorations of minerals focus on three properties: appearance, texture, and smell. Students apply their observing and describing skills to investigate these properties in each of the 12 minerals. They are then introduced to a method of systematically recording their observations. These activities deepen students' awareness of the differences among minerals. The experiences also prepare students for the next five lessons, during which they will test their minerals to identify and describe additional properties. Once the students have completed their tests, they will use the data they have collected to identify the minerals by name.

- Students observe, describe, and draw each mineral in their set.

- Students observe, describe, and record the texture and smell of each mineral.

- Students discuss the similarities and differences among minerals.

- Students discuss the different terms they used to describe the same property.

- Students set up their mineral profile sheets.

Background

In Lessons 7 through 11, students will learn some of the tests that geologists use to identify the properties of minerals. These tests are called **field tests** because geologists perform them when they are outdoors in the field. The first field test, in Lesson 7, involves examining the color of the streak that a mineral leaves when it is rubbed over a hard, porous surface. In subsequent lessons, students will explore the mineral's ability to transmit light, its luster, its hardness, and its response to a magnet.

Before doing these tests, students need an opportunity to become familiar with their minerals. They begin by sorting and describing the minerals on the basis of their own observations.

Next, the students focus on properties that can be identified with their senses of sight, touch, and smell. These observations will result in subjective descriptions that reflect each student's individual perception and vocabulary. The class discussions provide opportunities for students to develop their language skills and learn to accept the opinions of others. When students' observations differ, encourage them to exchange minerals and to compare descriptions again.

In this lesson, students will record their observations on a set of 12 mineral profile sheets. They will use these sheets throughout the next several lessons as a tool for organizing the data they have collected about each mineral. In Lesson 14, they will apply the data from the mineral profile sheets, along with information from the brief reading selections that follow each test, to identify each mineral by name. Each student will then put together the profile sheets to create his or her own "Minerals Field Guide."

After exploring the appearance, texture, and smell of their minerals, students read about sulfur. Soft sulfur has a distinctive smell; the hard, crystalline form of sulfur does not. All sulfur has a strong smell when it is burned.

Materials

For each student
- 1 science notebook
- 1 hand lens
- 12 **Mineral Profile Sheets** (blackline master)
- 1 pair of disposable gloves

For every two students
- 1 set of 12 minerals in an egg carton
- 1 cardboard tray
- 1 dropper
- 1 cup of water, 90 ml (3 oz)

For the class
- Class lists entitled "What We Know about Minerals" and "What We Want to Know about Minerals" (from Lesson 5)
- 1 colored marker
- Crayons or colored pencils that correspond to the colors of the minerals

Preparation

1. Make 12 copies of the blackline master **Mineral Profile Sheet** (pg. 61) for every student.

2. Wearing gloves, examine the 12 minerals to become familiar with their appearance, texture, and smell.

3. Place a small amount of water in each of the 15 plastic cups.

4. Read the information about sulfur on pg. 60 of this guide.

Procedure

1. Ask students to review their observations about minerals from Lesson 5. Use questions such as the following:

   - How were the minerals you examined different from each other?

   - How were the minerals similar?

2. Let students know that today they will again explore their collection of 12 minerals. They also will record their observations and discoveries.

3. Have one student from each pair collect a carton of minerals, a cardboard tray, a cup of water, a dropper, two pairs of disposable gloves, and two hand lenses. Ask the other student to take out colored pencils or crayons.

4. Allow time for the class to explore the 12 minerals by using their senses of sight, touch, and smell. Point out that putting a few drops of water on the minerals might help make it easier to detect a smell and to observe the color.

Figure 6-1

Exploring how minerals look, feel, and smell

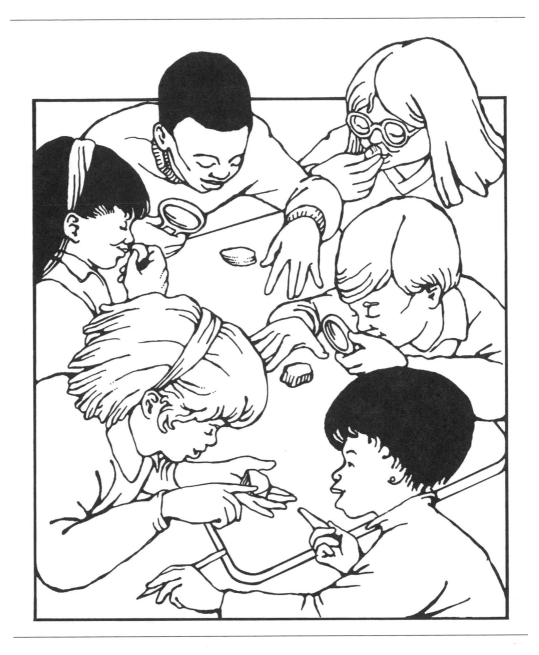

5. Distribute 12 copies of the **Mineral Profile Sheet** to each student. Ask the students to write the letters A to L after the word "Mineral" in the first box on each sheet. Explain that these 12 letters correspond to the letters on the 12 labeled minerals. Students will have one sheet for each mineral.

6. Let students know that they will use the 12 sheets during the next several lessons to organize and record information about each of the minerals in a systematic way. Later in the unit, students will put the profile sheets together to make their own "Minerals Field Guide." Today, students will record information on each sheet in the three spaces labeled "Mineral," "Feel," and "Smell."

7. Ask students to think about mineral A. What would they put in those three sections to describe it? Discuss and compare ideas. Have students use crayons or colored pencils to draw and color a picture of mineral A in the large space in the upper left corner of the appropriate mineral profile sheet. Then ask them to record information about the feel and smell of mineral A in the corresponding boxes on the sheet.

8. Now have students fill in the three boxes on sheets B to L for each of the remaining 11 minerals.

9. Ask students to place their mineral profile sheets in the pocket of their science notebooks, return their supplies to the materials center, throw away their gloves, and wash their hands.

Figure 6-2

Completed mineral profile sheet

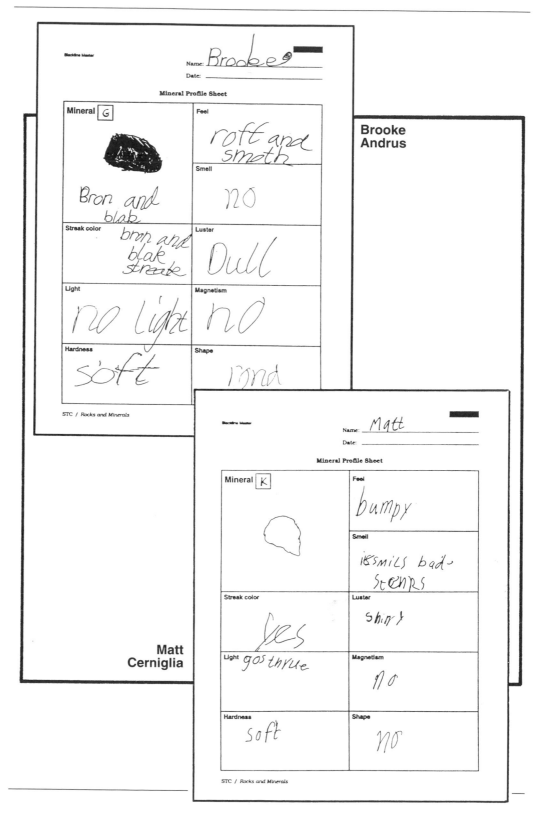

Figure 6-3

Recording how
minerals look, feel,
and smell

Final Activities

1. Review the class lists "What We Know about Minerals" and "What We Want to Know about Minerals." Record any new ideas with a different-colored marker.

2. Involve students in reading about sulfur on pg. 22 of the Student Activity Book (pg. 60 of the Teacher's Guide). They may do this as a class or in pairs.

Assessment

This lesson is the beginning of a series in which students will test their 12 minerals and record the results of those tests on mineral profile sheets. As the tests become more sophisticated, students' recordkeeping and interpretation of results will require increasing attention to detail.

Over the next seven lessons, watch for growth in the following skill areas.

Testing Procedures

■ Do student pairs share materials and work cooperatively?

■ Do students take responsibility for collecting and returning their materials to the materials center?

■ Do students follow directions in the use of materials?

■ Do students follow the written procedures for the tests?

■ Do students repeat a test when they question the results?

Recordkeeping

■ Do students match the mineral to the correct profile sheet?

■ Can students differentiate the test results among minerals?

■ Are students' recorded results consistent with their observed results?

■ Do summaries recorded in journals reflect recorded test results?

Discussions

■ Are students able to communicate their findings?

■ Do students compare and question results from other groups?

■ Do students refer to readings and the results of their tests when they make predictions about the identity of minerals?

Reading Selection

Sulfur

Have you ever smelled a rotten egg? When sulfur burns, it smells just like a rotten egg. In fact, rotten eggs have that smell because eggs contain sulfur! We need minerals such as sulfur in our food. It helps change food into energy and helps bones grow. When you eat eggs, onions, or cabbage, you are taking in sulfur. Where else do you think you might have smelled sulfur? When you watch fireworks on the Fourth of July, what do you think you are smelling? It's sulfur!

Sulfur is also used for making gunpowder, fertilizers, dynamite, and match heads. It's an important ingredient in many medicines. Did you know that sulfur was used during the Civil War and World War I to prevent wound infections?

Sulfur is found in many places. You can find sulfur crystals in some of the igneous rocks that form when volcanoes erupt. Sulfur is also found in limestone.

Which of your minerals do you think is sulfur?

Name: _____

Date: _____

Mineral Profile Sheet

Mineral ☐	Feel
	Smell
Streak color	**Luster**
Light	**Magnetism**
Hardness	**Shape**

Describing the Color of Minerals

Overview and Objectives

The properties of minerals that students observed and recorded in Lesson 6—appearance, texture, and smell—are similar to those they examined in rocks. In this lesson, students concentrate on a single property, color, as they are introduced to the first of five field tests that geologists use to identify minerals. After sorting the minerals on the basis of their observable color, students apply the streak test to discover each mineral's identifying color, which is not always the same as its observable color.

■ Students describe and record the observable color of the 12 minerals.

■ Students sort their minerals on the basis of observable color.

■ Students apply the streak test to their minerals.

■ Students describe and record the results of the streak test.

■ Students compare and discuss the differences between each mineral's observable color and its identifying (streak) color.

Background

Color is one of the first properties most students use to describe minerals. As they will discover, however, a mineral often cannot be conclusively identified on the basis of its **observable color,** or the color it appears to the unaided eye.

Observable color is inconclusive for two major reasons. First, several different minerals have the same observable color. Second, different samples of the same mineral have different observable colors. Pure quartz, for example, is clear; however, quartz may also be yellow, rose, gray, blue, or purple. Variations in observable color usually result from the mixing of very small amounts of other materials (impurities) with the mineral during its formation. For example, red amethyst is a variety of quartz that contains a tiny amount of iron.

The color of the powdered form of a mineral, or **identifying color,** is more consistent than its observable color. Geologists approximate the color of the powdered form of a mineral by wiping it across a hard, porous surface—typically, unglazed porcelain—to produce a "streak" of color.

Help your students get a feel for the appropriate amount of force to use when they rub the minerals over the streak plates. Tell them to rub gently. If they apply too much pressure, they may scratch the surface of the plate. If this happens, the mark they see may actually be bits of porcelain rather than the streak left by the powdered mineral.

After students perform the streak test on each of their minerals and record their results, they read about graphite and hematite, two minerals that often have similar observable colors but distinctive identifying colors.

Materials

For each student

  1 science notebook
  1 set of 12 **Mineral Profile Sheets** (from Lesson 6)
  1 pair of disposable gloves

For every two students

  1 set of 12 minerals in an egg carton
  1 cardboard tray
  1 white streak plate (unglazed porcelain tile)
  1 black streak plate (unglazed porcelain tile)
     Crayons or colored markers or pencils

For the classroom

     Dish detergent, liquid tile cleaner, and water
     Paper towels

Preparation

1. Review the **Student Instructions for Performing the Streak Test** on pg. 66 of this guide (pg. 25 of the Student Activity Book).

2. Wearing gloves, rub each of your minerals against the streak plates to familiarize yourself with the process and with any difference between the mineral's observable and identifying colors.

3. If the students' streak plates have been used before, clean them with soapy water and, if needed, a mild abrasive such as a liquid tile cleaner or baking soda.

4. Read the information about hematite and graphite on pg. 67 of this guide.

Procedure

1. Ask students to review the information they have recorded on their mineral profile sheets. Ask them to focus on one mineral as they think about the following questions:

   ■ What did you learn in the last lesson about that mineral?

   ■ What is one distinctive property of that mineral?

2. Now ask students to look at the colored picture they made for the mineral they have chosen. What word or words would they use to describe the color of the mineral? Let students know that they may look again at the mineral before they answer.

3. Have one student from each pair pick up the carton of minerals, tray, disposable gloves, and two streak plates from the materials center.

4. Ask students to sort their minerals on the basis of observable color. Have each pair of students share the way they sorted with another student team. Did both pairs sort their minerals in the same way? Encourage them to discuss the reasons for the differences.

5. Now review the **Student Instructions for Performing the Streak Test.** Demonstrate how to use the streak plate by gently rubbing one edge of a mineral sample on the porcelain tile. Point out to students that some streaks may show up better on the dark plate than on the light plate, and vice versa.

   Note: One stroke of the mineral will usually produce a streak. Additional strokes will only make it more difficult to clean the tile afterwards. Also, some students may find it necessary to clean their tiles once or twice during the testing of the 12 specimens.

6. Have the students perform the streak test with each of their minerals.

   Note: Students may want to make their streaks in the space labeled "Streak color" on the mineral profile sheet. This works well for soft minerals such as graphite, but not for harder minerals. Explain that students may record their observations in any way they wish. They may describe the color in words, use a colored marker or crayon to indicate the color, or stroke the mineral across the page.

7. Have students return their minerals, trays, and streak plates to the materials center and put away their colored pencils or crayons. Ask students to throw away their gloves and then to wash their hands.

Final Activities

1. Discuss the following questions:

   ■ Which minerals left a streak?

   ■ Was the color of the streak always the same as the color of the mineral?

2. Have students read the selections about hematite and graphite on pg. 26 of the Student Activity Book (pg. 67 of this guide). They may read as a class or in pairs.

3. Ask students to write at least two new things they have learned about minerals in their science notebooks.

Extensions

[LANGUAGE ARTS]

1. Have students read books or stories about American Indians and cave paintings. Ask your librarian to suggest appropriate titles.

[MATHEMATICS]

2. Involve the class in a "people-sorting" activity. Think of one student and identify attributes that he or she shares with many students, a few students, and no other student. State the attributes one at a time, beginning with the most general and moving to the most specific. After naming each attribute, invite the class to guess the identity of the student. Ask students to take turns leading the activity.

Student Instructions for Performing the Streak Test

1. Gently stroke one edge of mineral A across the surface of the white tile. Now stroke it over the black tile.

2. Record the color of the streak in the space labeled "Streak color" on the profile sheet for mineral A.

3. Repeat this test for each of the other 11 minerals. Record the color of the streak of each mineral on its profile sheet.

4. Wash the tile with water, soap, and a paper towel.

Reading Selections

Hematite

Hematite is found all over the world. Some forms of hematite look like a black, bumpy rock. They leave a gray or black streak.

Another type of hematite leaves a red-brown streak that looks like dried blood. Many early peoples, including American Indians in the Southwest United States, ground hematite into powder and mixed it with liquid to make a dark-red paint.

They covered the walls of caves with paintings of horses, buffaloes, and other animals. Today, hematite is still used to color paints.

But hematite has another major use. It is one of the minerals from which we get iron, one of the strongest of all metals.

Iron is the main ingredient in steel. It was discovered in Egypt about 3,000 years ago. That was when the "Iron Age" began. The discovery of iron was one of the most important events in the history of our civilization.

Can you find hematite in your set of minerals?

Graphite

Did you know that you hold graphite in your hand almost every day? Graphite is the "lead" in your pencil. The word "graphite" comes from the Greek word that means "to write." People began writing with sticks of graphite about 400 years ago. That caused a lot of dirty fingers!

But graphite still had a big advantage over ink—because it is so soft, it's easy to erase mistakes! The wooden pencil was invented in the late 1700s in France.

Graphite has many other uses that are related to its special properties. Graphite feels slippery. It is used for lubricants, which make machine parts slide over one another easily. Graphite can withstand very high temperatures, and it conducts electricity. For these reasons, it is used to make electrodes. Electrodes carry electricity from one place to another.

Do you think one of your minerals might be graphite? Can you describe its streak? How does it feel?

Shining a Light on the Minerals

Overview and Objectives

In this lesson, students are introduced to a new property of minerals—their ability to transmit light. As students shine a penlight on each mineral, they observe that some minerals are transparent, some are translucent, and others are opaque. The class discussion of how to describe and record this property expands students' vocabulary and reinforces their awareness that people may use different words to describe the same observation. Students will again test their minerals with light in Lesson 9, where they are introduced to another property, luster.

- Students test how much light shines through each of their minerals.

- Students compare and discuss each mineral's ability to transmit light.

- Students sort the minerals according to their ability to transmit light.

- Students record the results of the light test.

Background

Although the concept that students explore in this lesson is quite simple, the term used to describe it, "light transmissivity," is not. This term has been shortened to "Light" on the mineral profile sheets.

Most students will be able to decide quickly whether they can see light through each mineral, but they may not have the vocabulary to describe their observations. During the first part of this lesson, you will have to give students time to suggest their own words to describe what they see and to develop a shared understanding of the meaning of the words they use to describe their observations.

The three descriptors that geologists use to describe a mineral's light transmissivity are opaque, translucent, and transparent. Many minerals are **opaque;** they transmit no light. Others are **translucent;** they transmit varying degrees of light. Some minerals are **transparent;** they transmit virtually all the light that is shined at them.

After students have tested each of their minerals with a penlight and recorded and discussed their results, they will read about calcite and muscovite, both of which display unique properties of light transmissivity.

Materials

For each student

  1 science notebook

  1 set of 12 **Mineral Profile Sheets** (from Lesson 6)

  1 pair of disposable gloves

For every two students

1 set of 12 minerals in an egg carton
1 cardboard tray
1 square of transparent film, 75 × 75 mm (3 × 3 in)
1 square of waxed paper, 75 × 75 mm (3 × 3 in)
1 square of cardboard, 75 × 75 mm (3 × 3 in)
1 penlight

Preparation

1. Cut out 75-mm (3-in) squares of transparent film, waxed paper, and cardboard. Every pair of students will need one square of each of the different materials.

2. Review the **Student Instructions for Performing the Light Test** on pg. 72 of this guide (pg. 29 of the Student Activity Book). Following these procedures (and wearing gloves), test your set of 12 minerals to determine whether each mineral is opaque, translucent, or transparent.

3. Test the penlights. Replace batteries if necessary.

4. Read the information about calcite and muscovite on pg. 73 of this guide.

Procedure

1. Give every pair of students one square each of transparent film, waxed paper, and cardboard. Ask them to place each square over a different part of the first page of Lesson 8 of their Student Activity Books. Are they able to see through all the squares and read the passage to their partners?

Figure 8-1

Exploring with the squares

2. Ask students to describe what happened when they tried to see through the three squares.

   ■ How are the squares different (for example, shape, size, thickness, material)?

   ■ Which square was easiest to read through?

   ■ Which was hardest to read through?

   ■ How might the differences among the squares be related to the problems students had seeing through them?

3. Help the students decide on three terms they can use to describe the quality of each of the squares that makes it easy or hard to see the print through it. They will apply these terms to their mineral specimens. For minerals that are transparent, they might choose an adjective such as "clear"; for translucent minerals, "cloudy"; for opaque minerals, "dark." They also may choose to describe how much light they see, using phrases such as "a lot of light," "a little light," and "no light."

4. Ask one student from each pair to collect their carton of minerals, disposable gloves, and a cardboard tray from the materials center. Pass out the penlights. Give students a few minutes to practice shining their penlights on nearby objects.

5. Review the **Student Instructions for Performing the Light Test.** Have students perform the test. As they complete their mineral profile sheets, ask them to use the terms they have just agreed on with their classmates.

6. Ask students to place their minerals into three groups on the basis of how much light they saw. Have different student pairs compare their groupings. Discuss differences in grouping and problems the students might have encountered in deciding how to sort their minerals.

7. Have students return their minerals, trays, and penlights to the materials center. Ask students to throw away their gloves and then to wash their hands.

Final Activities

1. Ask students to read the information on muscovite and calcite on pg. 30 of the Student Activity Book (pg. 73 of this guide).

2. Finally, ask students to think about the importance of a mineral's ability to transmit light and how it might relate to the uses of some minerals. Ask them to write their ideas in their science notebooks.

Extensions

LANGUAGE ARTS

1. Challenge students to find several objects at home for each of the three descriptors they developed in class. Ask students to make a list of these objects and to bring some of them to class.

SCIENCE

2. Encourage students to find out how glass is made.

SOCIAL STUDIES

3. Have students research how glass objects have changed over the decades. Set up a learning center and ask the students to bring in glass objects of different types and styles. Connect the type and style of the glass with the culture and history of that time.

Student Instructions for Performing the Light Test

1. Pick up mineral A. Shine the penlight on it.

2. Observe how much light shines through the mineral. Some? A lot? None at all?

3. Using the terms you have agreed on in class, record results in the space labeled "Light" on your mineral profile sheet.

4. Repeat Steps 1, 2, and 3 for the other 11 minerals.

Reading Selections

Calcite

Have you ever been in a cave and seen the formations that look like icicles? They are called stalactites and stalagmites.

These are rocks that contain a lot of calcite. Calcite is one of the most important minerals found in rocks formed under water. Calcite is also found in clam shells. Sometimes calcite is white. Sometimes it is so clear that you can see through it.

One kind of clear calcite is called Iceland spar. It has an unusual property. If you placed it on these words, you would see a double image! Because of this property, calcite is used in some kinds of prisms and microscopes.

Which mineral do you think is calcite?

Muscovite

Muscovite is a shiny, silvery-white mineral that has many thin sheets, like the pages in a book. Before glass was easily available, many people in Russia used pieces of muscovite to make windows. The name "Moscow," the capital city of Russia, comes from the Russian word for "glass." Did you know that people from Moscow are called "Muscovites"?

Which mineral do you think is muscovite?

Exploring the Luster of Minerals

Overview and Objectives

Having observed the amount of light they could see through each of their minerals, students examine a second property related to how minerals interact with light: luster. The students' review of all the information they have recorded on their mineral profile sheets strengthens their understanding that each mineral has certain properties that make it possible to distinguish it from others.

- Students observe, discuss, and describe the luster of minerals when they are placed under bright light.

- Students sort their minerals according to similarities and differences in luster.

- Students record the results of the luster test on their mineral profile sheets.

- Students summarize the information they have recorded on each mineral and begin to identify its distinguishing properties.

Background

A mineral's luster, or shine, depends on the way its surface reflects light. Minerals that reflect light like polished metal are said to have a **metallic** luster. All other minerals have a **nonmetallic** luster. Geologists distinguish among several nonmetallic lusters: dull, waxy, pearly, and brilliant. The terms used to describe luster are difficult to define because they rely on individual perceptions and language. To make their descriptions of luster as useful as possible, geologists use specific minerals for comparisons.

To help students develop a common set of words that they can use in describing the luster of their minerals, shine a penlight on various objects in the classroom, one at a time, and ask students to describe how the objects look. To illustrate a metallic luster, such as that of galena, shine the light on an unpainted metal table leg or a pencil sharpener. As an illustration of a dull luster, such as that of gypsum, shine the light on the wall. Use a window as an example of glassy luster, similar to that of quartz. Make sure your students understand that not everyone will see objects in the same way. At the same time, help them try to reach agreement on the terms they will use when they apply the luster test to their minerals.

At the end of the lesson, students read about galena and gypsum, two minerals that have distinctive lusters.

Materials

For each student
1   science notebook
1   set of 12 **Mineral Profile Sheets**
1   pair of disposable gloves

For every two students
1   copy of the blackline master **Sorting Minerals by Luster**
1   set of 12 minerals in an egg carton
1   cardboard tray
1   penlight

For the class
1   sheet of newsprint
1   colored marker
   Examples of objects with metallic luster: foil wrap, metal spoon, jar lid
   Examples of objects with waxy luster: polished shoe, plastic margarine tub
   Examples of objects with glassy luster: drinking glass, vase, eyeglasses
   Examples of objects with dull luster: eraser, unfinished wooden block

Preparation

1. Make sure that all the penlights are working. Replace batteries if needed.

2. Identify objects in the classroom that have different lusters when illuminated by a penlight. Examples include a table leg (metallic), window (glassy), floor (waxy), and chalkboard (dull).

3. Draw an enlarged version of the blackline master **Sorting Minerals by Luster** (pg. 80) onto a sheet of newsprint. Title the newsprint "Ways to Describe the Luster of an Object." Divide the chart into four squares and label them "metallic," "glassy," "waxy," and "dull."

4. Make one copy of the blackline master **Sorting Minerals by Luster** for each student pair.

5. Review the **Student Instructions for Performing the Luster Test** on pg. 78 of this guide (pg. 33 of the Student Activity Book). Wearing gloves, determine the luster of each of the 12 minerals.

6. Read the information about galena and gypsum on pg. 79 of this guide.

Procedure

1. Review observations students have made and results of the tests they have done thus far by asking questions such as the following:

   ■ Which minerals have a special smell?

   ■ Which minerals have a special feel or texture?

   ■ Which minerals have a streak color that is different from their observable color?

   ■ Which minerals can you see light through?

2. Let students know that today they will perform a second test with their penlights to learn about another property of minerals: luster. Explain that luster refers to how the surface of an object looks when light is shined on it. Show the chart on which you have written the words "metallic," "glassy," "waxy," and "dull."

3. Darken the room. Illuminate several metallic objects with the penlight. Ask students which word on the chart best describes the luster of those objects. Help students reach agreement.

Note: Try to keep the amount of light that you shine on the object constant. If not, students may focus on the size of the circle of light rather than on how the illuminated object looks.

4. Repeat Step 3 with the waxy, glassy, and dull objects. Turn the lights on.

5. Ask one student from each pair to collect their carton of minerals, two pairs of disposable gloves, and a cardboard tray while you distribute penlights.

6. Review the **Student Instructions for Performing the Luster Test.** Turn the lights off again. Ask students to follow the directions to test the luster of each mineral. Listen for, and encourage students to use, the terms from the class list.

7. Turn on the lights. As a group, discuss the students' descriptions of the luster of each mineral. If necessary, compare the mineral with some of the classroom objects used at the beginning of the lesson.

Note: Different samples of the same mineral may have different lusters; in fact, different parts of the sample may even have different lusters. Therefore, it may be valid for students to describe one end of a quartz crystal as "glassy" and the other end as "waxy." If students ask, explain that these differences are caused by impurities in the minerals, the way the specimen broke when it was collected, or simply the way the mineral was formed.

8. Have students return their minerals to the materials center, throw away their gloves, and wash their hands. Collect the penlights.

Final Activities

1. Ask students to read the information on pg. 34 of the Student Activity Book (pg. 79 of this guide) about galena and gypsum, each of which has a distinctive luster.

2. Now have students quietly review all the information they have about each mineral. Ask them to think about which pieces of information they could use to describe a mineral in a way that would allow someone else to identify it from a collection of minerals.

3. Ask students which minerals they now think they can identify by name. Encourage them to focus on matching the information they have recorded on their mineral profile sheets with information from the reading selections. Make sure students know that they will learn the names of all of their minerals after they have completed all of the tests.

Extensions

LANGUAGE ARTS

1. Ask students to apply their new vocabulary and observation skills by identifying objects in their homes that have the same luster as those described in class. Have students write a description of the objects to share in class the following day.

MATHEMATICS

2. Make a "real graph" with categories that correspond to the descriptors chosen by the class. Ask students to find objects to hang on the graph for each category (for example, buttons, jar lids, plastic spoons, foil, waxed paper, paper cups).

Student Instructions for Performing the Luster Test

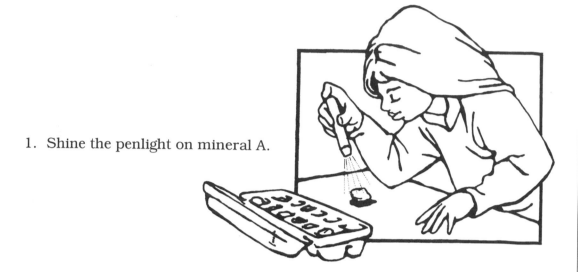

1. Shine the penlight on mineral A.

2. How does the mineral look under the light? Place it in one of the boxes on your sorting sheet.

3. Record the word from that box in the space marked "Luster" on your profile sheet for mineral A.

4. Repeat Steps 1, 2, and 3 with the remaining 11 minerals.

Reading Selections

Galena

Galena is shiny and very soft. You can scratch it with your fingernail. It melts and can be molded into shapes. If it breaks, it separates into small cubes.

Galena contains lead, which is a common metal. Hundreds of years ago, some people believed that lead could keep away evil spirits. They stored their jewels and religious objects in chests made of lead. Today, we know that lead really does keep out something that may be harmful—radiation. That's why we keep radioactive materials in lead containers. The walls in nuclear power plants are made of lead.

Lead has other uses. Mixed with tin, it is used to cover and protect underground electrical cables. It is also used in batteries.

We have to be careful about how we use lead. We now know that it is also a poison. Lead used to be added to gasoline, for example, because it kept the car's engine running smoothly. Because the lead fumes were dangerous to the environment, lead is no longer used in gasoline. Lead also was once used in most paints. Because it can be poisonous if eaten, lead is no longer used in house paints.

Can you find galena in your minerals? Can you describe its luster?

Gypsum

Gypsum looks dull and earthy. It is usually found in small pieces. These pieces are ground up and used to make plaster of Paris. Have you seen plaster of Paris? What color is it?

Casts for broken bones used to be made from gypsum. Today, gypsum is used to construct walls in homes and buildings. The building material called "drywall" is really "gypsum board."

Artists sometimes use large pieces of a special kind of gypsum to carve beautiful statues. The name of this special gypsum is alabaster. It is pink or white. Have you ever seen an alabaster statue? It looks a lot like polished plaster!

Is gypsum in your set of minerals? What color was its streak?

Sorting Minerals by Luster

Place each mineral in one box.

Metallic	Glassy
Dull	**Waxy**

Exploring the Hardness of Minerals

Overview and Objectives

In Lessons 8 and 9, students were introduced to the concept of comparing their observations with standards in order to describe two properties of minerals. Building on this concept, students use two additional standards, a copper penny and a steel nail, to explore another property of minerals—hardness. Through reading about two minerals and discussing information about the hardness test, students begin to realize that the properties of minerals often help determine how they can be used.

- Students test, compare, and discuss the hardness of 12 minerals.

- Students sort minerals according to their relative hardness.

- Students record the results of the hardness test.

Background

Hardness, or resistance to scratching, is an important property of minerals. A mineral's use is often related to its hardness.

Scientists classify the hardness of minerals using the **Mohs scale,** a standard that is based on the concept that the harder of two minerals will scratch the softer. Each point on the Mohs scale is represented by a mineral of known hardness (see Figure 10–1). When classifying a mineral, scientists compare it with this 10-point scale and give it a ranking from 1 (soft, like talc) to 10 (hard, like a diamond).

In this lesson, students do not actually use the Mohs scale to compare the hardness of the 12 minerals; instead, they use a copper penny and a steel nail as standards. Students then classify the minerals as soft, medium, or hard.

After testing their minerals, students read about two minerals: diamonds and talc.

Materials

For each student
- 1 science notebook
- 1 set of 12 **Mineral Profile Sheets**
- 1 hand lens
- 1 pair of disposable gloves

For every two students
- 1 set of 12 minerals in an egg carton
- 1 copper penny
- 1 steel nail
- 1 copy of **Minerals—Soft, Medium, or Hard** (blackline master)

Figure 10-1

Mohs Scale of Hardness

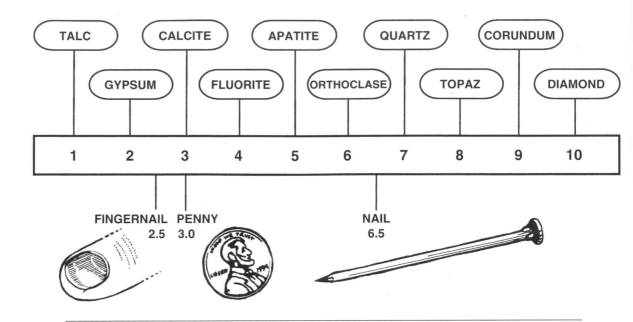

Preparation

1. Make one copy of the blackline master **Minerals—Soft, Medium, or Hard** (pg. 89) for each pair of students.

2. Review the **Student Instructions for Performing the Hardness Test** on pg. 87 in the Teacher's Guide (pg. 37 of the Student Activity Book). Wearing gloves, test your set of minerals to determine their hardness.

   Note: Learn to distinguish between scratching and breaking. Some minerals that fracture easily may chip under pressure without even being scratched.

3. Arrange the supplies in the materials center.

4. Read the information about diamonds and talc on pg. 88 of this guide.

Procedure

1. Introduce the concept of hardness by asking students to think of a hard object.

   ■ How does it look and feel?

   ■ Which of their minerals do they think could be called hard?

   ■ Which minerals could be called soft?

2. Show students a penny and a nail. Invite them to tell you what they know about each. Are they hard? Which is harder?

   Suppose they scratched the penny with the nail. What would happen? What might this mean?

3. Have students follow along as you read the **Student Instructions for Performing the Hardness Test.**

4. Demonstrate how to use a copper penny to scratch a mineral sample. Soft minerals can easily be destroyed by scratching, so encourage students to scratch gently. Then demonstrate how to scratch a mineral with a nail.

5. Distribute a copy of the blackline master **Minerals—Soft, Medium, or Hard** to each pair of students. Discuss the three terms.

   ■ Soft: Can be scratched by a penny

   ■ Medium: Cannot be scratched by a penny but can be scratched by a nail

   ■ Hard: Cannot be scratched by a penny or a nail

6. Ask one student from each pair to pick up the carton of minerals and disposable gloves from the materials center while you distribute the nails and pennies.

Safety Note: Caution the students to be careful not to scratch themselves or the furniture when using the nail.

---

7. Allow students time to test and record the hardness of each mineral.

8. Ask students to return their minerals and hand lenses to the materials center, throw away their gloves, and wash their hands. Have them return their mineral profile sheets to their science notebooks. Collect the nails, pennies, and blackline masters.

Final Activities

1. Ask students to share their findings with other members of the class. Students may have sorted the minerals in different ways. Ask for possible reasons for these differences. Students' reasons might include:

   ■ Differences among the samples

   ■ Different scratching techniques

   ■ Mistakes in recording

   If some students' results differed from those of their classmates, give them the nail and penny and allow them time to retest the minerals.

2. Ask students to think about the differences in hardness among the minerals. Do the soft minerals share any other property? (They should all show a distinct streak.) Do all the hard minerals share any other property? (They should show no streak.)

3. Ask students to read and discuss the information on diamonds and talc on pg. 38 in the Student Activity Book (pg. 88 of this guide).

4. Can students now identify any minerals by name? Which ones? Why?

Extensions

SCIENCE

1. Students may enjoy arranging their minerals in order, from softest to hardest, to create their own scale.

   ■ Ask students to rub each of the minerals in the "Soft" group against one another. The mineral that is scratched by all of the others is the softest and should be placed first in line.

   ■ Repeat this step with the remaining soft minerals to identify the next softest sample. Place this one next to the softest.

   ■ Continue until the soft minerals are placed in order.

   ■ Use the same procedure to place "Medium" and "Hard" minerals in order.

SCIENCE

2. In this lesson, students used a penny and a nail as the standards for sorting the minerals into three groups. Students may enjoy choosing their own standard (for example, a fingernail, a paper clip, or a nickel) and grouping the minerals according to it.

Student Instructions for Performing the Hardness Test

1. Scratch your sample of mineral A with the copper penny.

   Note: Scratch the minerals gently. You may damage some of them if you scratch them too hard.

2. If the penny left a scratch on the mineral, place it in the space labeled "Soft" on your **Minerals—Soft, Medium, or Hard** sheet. If the penny did not scratch the mineral, put it back in the carton.

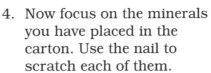

3. Test the remaining 11 minerals with the penny. Place each of them in the appropriate space on the sheet or back in the carton.

4. Now focus on the minerals you have placed in the carton. Use the nail to scratch each of them.

5. If the nail scratches a mineral, put it in the space on the sheet that is labeled "Medium." If the nail does not scratch the mineral, place it in the space labeled "Hard."

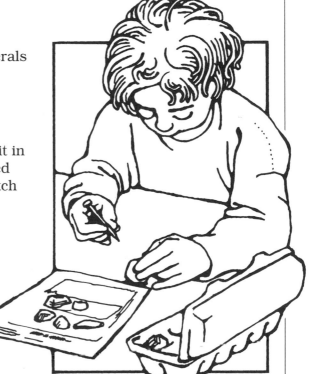

6. Record your results for each mineral in the space labeled "Hardness" on the mineral profile sheets.

Reading Selections

Diamonds

Diamonds are the hardest of all minerals. They were formed long ago in igneous rocks. Today, we mine diamonds in places near extinct volcanoes. But diamonds are also found near old riverbeds. How do you suppose the diamonds got there? Believe it or not, diamonds have even been found in meteorites from outer space!

You probably know that diamonds are used in jewelry. But did you know they are also used in industry? In fact, out of every five diamonds found, only one is used to make jewelry. The others are used for industrial purposes.

For example, diamonds are used to cut, drill, and polish other materials. Powerful drills with diamond tips are used for drilling oil wells. Wire containing diamond bits is used to cut blocks of stone from mining quarries. Diamond powder is used for polishing hard materials such as glass. Surgeons use small knives with diamond blades for delicate eye operations.

Do you think you have a diamond in your set of minerals?

Talc

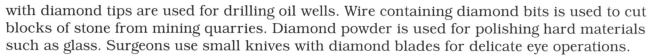

Talc is one of the softest of all minerals. It has a waxy luster and a slippery feel. It looks like chalk. You may be able to guess one use for talc: to make baby powder. Talc is also used to make ceramics and pottery.

Because talc resists acid, it is used to make sinks and countertops for chemical laboratories. Talc is a major component of soapstone, a soft rock that is also used to make tabletops.

Can you tell by feeling which of your minerals is talc?

Minerals—Soft, Medium, or Hard

Soft

Medium

Hard

Testing the Minerals with a Magnet

Overview and Objectives

In Lessons 7 to 10, students performed field tests to explore the color, transparency, luster, and hardness of minerals. They recorded their findings and results in their own terms, which reflected their personal perceptions. In this lesson, students are introduced to a test that has conclusive, "yes-no" results: testing with a magnet identifies magnetite. Students continue developing their problem-solving skills as they apply the results of this test to make inferences about the identities of their minerals.

- Students test minerals with a magnet and observe and describe the results.
- Students record and compare results of their test.
- Students read to learn more about magnetite.

Background

Scientists use positive and negative tests to identify the presence or absence of a property. Students will perform such a test in this lesson. The test is negative for most minerals; in other words, it produces no discernible results. Nonetheless, the test does provide conclusive information for identifying those few minerals that are magnetic. Geologists use this test to identify minerals in rocks. The results help them determine how the rocks can be used.

Three commonly found minerals are magnetic; of these, **magnetite** is the only one in the students' set. This special property of magnetite has made it important for centuries as a magnet and compass. At the end of this lesson, students will learn more about one form of magnetite, called lodestone, by reading "Lodestones Lead the Way."

Materials

For each student
  1 science notebook
  1 set of 12 **Mineral Profile Sheets**
  1 pair of disposable gloves

For every two students
  1 set of 12 minerals in an egg carton
  1 magnet

Preparation

1. Read the **Student Instructions for Performing the Magnetism Test** on pg. 93 of the Teacher's Guide (pg. 41 of the Student Activity Book). Wearing gloves, perform the test on each of the 12 minerals.

2. Arrange the supplies in the materials center.

Procedure

1. Review the information students have collected and reported on their mineral profile sheets by asking them to think of the property or test that has given them the most interesting or useful information about each mineral. Encourage them to share their ideas.

2. Discuss the variety of their responses. Relate their oral comments to the information they have recorded on the record sheets. Ask students whether they have described their minerals using similar words.

3. Let students know that today they will test their minerals with a magnet.

4. With the class, review the **Student Instructions for Performing the Magnetism Test.**

5. Have students pick up their minerals and gloves as you distribute the magnets. Allow time for students to explore with the magnets. Then ask them to proceed with the magnetism test.

6. Collect the minerals and magnets. Ask students to throw away their gloves and wash their hands.

Final Activities

1. Ask students to share their test results. Were they surprised? Why?

2. Then ask students to read and discuss "Lodestones Lead the Way," on pgs. 42–43 in the Student Activity Book (pgs. 94–95 of the Teacher's Guide).

3. Finally, ask students to think about what they now know about minerals and to write three new ideas in their science notebooks.

Extensions

| SCIENCE |

1. Have students perform the magnet test on the set of 12 rocks. Challenge them to explain what it might mean to a geologist if the magnet sticks to a rock.

| SCIENCE |

2. Bring in compasses for students to explore. Then go outside and practice using and reading the compass in the schoolyard.

| MATHEMATICS |

3. Hold a treasure hunt in your classroom or multipurpose room. Include directions that combine use of a compass and a meterstick. For example:

- Go west 2 meters.

- Turn north, go 75 centimeters.

- Turn southeast, go 3 meters.

Student Instructions for Performing the Magnetism Test

1. Hold up mineral A. Touch the magnet to it. Does the mineral stick to the magnet? Record your results in the space labeled "Magnetism" on the mineral profile sheet for mineral A.

2. Test each of the other 11 minerals with the magnet in the same way. Record the results on your mineral profile sheets.

Reading Selection

Lodestones Lead the Way

The magnetic compass is one of the most important inventions of all time. Before it was invented, sailors had only the sun, moon, stars, and local winds to guide them as they set out for faraway lands. The compass changed that. It pointed to the north pole. And once you know which way is north, you can figure out where south, east, and west are as well! A mineral called **lodestone,** which is a highly magnetized form of magnetite, makes the compass work.

Who discovered lodestone? No one really knows. According to some stories, it was discovered by shepherds in Asia, who noticed that the iron nails in their sandals sometimes clung to the ground as they walked across a field with rocks that contained lodestone.

The shepherds were amazed by this. They probably picked up some samples of the mineral and began to tell other people about their discovery. The news spread.

One of the first written references to the mysterious powers of the lodestone is in a book written in China. Around the year A.D. 1000, the Chinese began to use lodestones to guide ships at sea. They did this because of an amazing discovery. If you place a lodestone on a small piece of wood and float it in a cup of water, the lodestone always lines up in a north-south direction! And if you touch the lodestone to an iron needle for long enough, the needle, too, lines up in a north-south direction. The magnetic compass had been invented.

Sailors in Europe started to use the compass about 800 years ago. Then, they gave the lodestone its name. Lode meant "to lead."

For centuries, people believed that the lodestone had secret powers. Magicians used it to tell fortunes. People thought it could cure illness. Sailors believed that onion and garlic would destroy the magnetic force, so they never ate these foods while they were at sea. Because so many seamen feared the powers of the magnetized needle, the ship's pilot kept it hidden away in a special box.

Little by little, these fears disappeared. The compass was brought out on deck, where all the sailors could use it. Christopher Columbus packed extra magnetic needles for his trips across the Atlantic Ocean in late 1400s. Ferdinand Magellan, the first person to sail around the world, carried 35 needles on his flagship!

What if those extra needles lost their magnetic power?

The captain always carried a precious piece of lodestone—to lead his crew safely to new adventures and new lands.

Describing the Shape of Minerals

Overview and Objectives

In this final lesson on the properties of minerals, students complete their profile sheets by recording the shape of each of the minerals. As students observe and describe four new mineral samples, they learn that some mineral samples have a distinctive shape and others do not. They are also confronted with the idea that a single mineral can display distinctly different shapes. These explorations of shape provide an intuitive introduction to the concept of crystalline structure in minerals. In the next lesson, students will further explore shape and other properties, as they compare and contrast several samples of the same minerals.

- Students observe and describe the shapes of four new mineral samples.

- Students compare the shapes of the 12 minerals in their set and the new samples.

- Students sort the 12 minerals on the basis of shape.

- Students discuss and record the shapes of their 12 minerals.

Background

The shape and size of a mineral are the result of its chemical composition, the length of time it took to cool and solidify, and the space available during its formation. Some mineral samples show a definite shape, or crystal form. Other samples are amorphous; in other words, they lack a crystal form.

Almost all minerals, regardless of their outward shape, have a regular internal geometric pattern, or crystalline structure. Six different crystal systems, or families, have been identified in minerals. All samples of the same mineral have the same internal crystalline structure even though the visible shape of a mineral and the size of its crystals may vary from sample to sample.

The crystalline structure of a mineral determines how it breaks or splits. Some minerals always break into the same distinctive shape. Halite breaks into cubes; micas, such as biotite and muscovite, break into very thin layers. The process of breaking into distinct shapes is called **cleavage.** The flat surfaces visible on some of the specimens, such as feldspar, or inside the clear ones, such as calcite, are cleavage planes along which the specimen broke or would break further if struck with enough force. Some minerals, including talc, hematite, and quartz, break into nondistinct shapes. The absence of cleavage is called **fracture.** The characteristics of cleavage and fracture are important in the identification of minerals.

Each of the four new mineral samples that students will examine in this lesson has a different shape. The halite, mineral M, is clear and has a cubelike shape.

The three varieties of gypsum, labeled N, O, and S, are quite different. Mineral N, satin spar, displays masses of small, glistening crystals that seem to be aligned in rows. Mineral O has distinctive round-edged, bladed crystals in a petal-like pattern; for this reason, it is popularly called "desert rose." Mineral S is a clear selenite crystal.

Until the middle of this century, all minerals were thought to have a crystalline structure, and many textbooks still state that all minerals are crystals. Electron microscopy has now revealed that a few "minerals" do not have a crystalline structure. Debate continues as to whether these should be referred to as minerals or "mineraloids."

Materials

For each student

1   science notebook
1   set of **12 Mineral Profile Sheets**
1   hand lens
1   pair of disposable gloves

For every two students

1   set of 12 minerals in an egg carton
1   halite sample (labeled M)
1   gypsum sample (satin spar variety, labeled N)
1   gypsum sample (bladed selenite crystal aggregate in "desert rose" form, labeled O)
1   gypsum sample (clear selenite crystal, labeled S)
1   cardboard tray
1   piece of manila paper, 10 × 15 cm (4 × 6 in)
1   penlight

For the class

1   sheet of newsprint, 60 × 90 cm (24 × 36 in)
1   colored marker

Preparation

1. Prepare a piece of manila paper measuring 10 × 15 cm (4 × 6 in) for each student pair. Students will place their minerals on these sheets when they observe their shapes.

2. Examine several samples of minerals M, N, O, and S to become familiar with their shapes.

3. Review the information on the mineral identification cards at the end of Lesson 14. Compare the shape of the minerals in your set with the descriptions on the cards.

4. Arrange the supplies in the materials center.

5. Read the information about quartz and fluorite on pg. 101 of this guide.

Procedure

1. Ask students to share what they know about crystals. What minerals have they seen in crystal form? Where did they see them?

2. Distribute the manila paper, hand lenses, disposable gloves, and samples of minerals M, N, O, and S. Allow students time to explore.

3. Ask the students whether they can see crystals in any of the minerals. Let them know that some minerals can be found as single, large crystals. The crystals in other minerals are so small that they cannot even be seen under a hand lens.

4. Invite students to share their observations. Point out that samples N, O, and S are all varieties of the same mineral. Then ask students how these samples are alike and different.

5. Have students pick up the remaining materials.

6. Ask students to use their hand lenses and penlights to look at the minerals closely.

   ■ Arc any of the minerals in the set shaped something like the four new samples?

   ■ Are there any minerals in the set whose shape does not resemble that of any of the new samples?

   ■ When you look at the minerals with the hand lens or under the penlight, do you see any special shapes that are different from the shape of the sample itself?

7. Now ask students to examine and sort their 12 minerals into groups on the basis of similar shape.

8. Encourage pairs of students to compare how they sorted their mineral samples.

9. Then ask students to suggest words to describe the shape of each mineral specimen and record their ideas on newsprint. Encourage the class to reach a consensus on words that describe the shapes of the minerals. Let students know that "no special shape" is a valid observation.

10. Now ask the students to use words, drawings, or both to record the shape of each specimen on its profile sheet.

11. Have students return the minerals and other supplies to the materials center, throw away their gloves, and wash their hands.

Final Activities

1. In pairs or as a class, have students read and discuss the information about quartz and fluorite on pg. 47 of the Student Activity Book (pg. 101 of this guide).

2. Ask students to write at least three things that they have learned about the shape of minerals in their science notebooks.

Extensions

MATHEMATICS

1. Use mathematical materials such as Polydrons™ or Googolplex™ to build a variety of three-dimensional geometric shapes. Discuss the number and shapes of the faces.

MATHEMATICS   ART

2. Have students construct crystal shapes from paper and make them into mobiles.

SCIENCE

3. Have students grow salt crystals. Follow the directions on pg. 100.

LANGUAGE ARTS

4. Use a book such as *Gems in the Smithsonian,* by Paul Desautels, as a source of information on minerals that are valuable because of their crystalline structure (see Bibliography).

Instructions for Growing Salt Crystals

Materials

> **Safety Tip:** Do this activity only when an adult is present.

Water, 240 ml (1 cup)
Granulated salt, 240 ml (1 cup)
Measuring cup
Small saucepan
Wooden spoon
Glass or jelly jar
Cotton string, 20 cm (8 in)
Pencil
Stove (source of heat)
Small weight (e.g., a metal nut, small washer, paper clip, or button)

Instructions

1. Make sure that all your equipment is clean.

2. Place the water in the pan and put the pan on the stove. Turn the heat on medium.

3. When the water boils, turn off the heat.

4. Add a spoonful of salt right away. Stir. Keep adding salt and stirring. When some salt sits on the bottom of the pan even after you stir it, stop adding salt.

5. Let the salt water cool.

6. Pour the salt water into the glass.

7. Wet the string. Tie the weight to the end of the string.

8. Tie the other end of the string around the middle of the pencil. Adjust the length of the string so that when you place the pencil across the top of the glass, the weight will hang just above the bottom of the glass.

9. Lay the pencil across the top of the glass. Hang the string in the salt water.

10. Put the glass in a place where it will not be disturbed.

11. Let the glass stand for three to five days. Check it every day. Remove the crystals that form on the surface of the water so that the water can continue to evaporate. Watch what grows on the string!

12. Discuss your results with your adult partner.

Reading Selections

Quartz

Quartz can be one of the prettiest and most colorful of all minerals. Some types of quartz are made up of tiny crystals, but many types display large crystals. Quartz crystals can be clear, purple, brown, or yellow. They are always six-sided, or hexagonal.

Quartz crystals are valued for their beauty. They are often used in jewelry. Geodes are rocks that are lined with crystals. In many cases, these crystals are quartz. Some geodes are bigger than basketballs! Have you ever seen a geode on a desk or bookshelf?

Quartz crystals have many commercial uses. Crystals are used in watches and clocks. The quartz crystals in your wristwatch vibrate more than 30,000 times a second! Quartz crystals are also used in radios, computers, microwave ovens, and VCRs.

Which crystal do you think is quartz?

Fluorite

Fluorite crystals are shaped like cubes. Sometimes the crystals are so tiny that you can't see them. Fluorite can be clear, yellow, purple, blue, or pale green.

Fluorite is a rather soft and brittle mineral. It is often used for industrial purposes. When fluorite is ground up, it is used as a chemical. This chemical has many uses. It is used in the manufacture of steel to help the melting process. And it even helps fight tooth decay! Fluorite is the source of fluoride, which is probably in your toothpaste.

Do you think you have a fluorite crystal in your set of minerals?

Comparing Samples of the Same Mineral

Overview and Objectives

Students begin this lesson by reflecting on what they have learned about each mineral. As they review their mineral profile sheets and summarize the properties of each mineral, students clarify and refine their written observations. To expand their knowledge, students then focus on the similarities and differences among several samples of each mineral. These experiences prepare them for Lesson 14, in which they will be challenged to identify each mineral by name.

- Students review and summarize what they have learned about the 12 minerals.

- Students identify distinctive properties of each mineral and use them to describe the mineral.

- Students compare and contrast several samples of the same mineral.

- Students reflect on their new observations of minerals and share ideas and questions about them.

Background

Identifying minerals can be difficult, even to the trained eye, because samples of the same mineral often look quite different. These variations in appearance may be due to differences in size, the presence of other minerals, and weathering. A single mineral can also be found in different shapes.

In order to truly "know" a mineral, it is necessary to have experience over time with a great many samples of it. To better familiarize themselves with minerals, geologists focus on distinctive properties present in all samples of a mineral they have observed as well as distinguishing properties that are absent in all samples of that mineral. The latter may be more difficult to discern than the former; this is where experience is especially helpful. As noted in earlier lessons, minerals can often be identified only with special chemical tests and X-ray techniques.

The mineral samples in this unit are relatively uniform. They represent only a fraction of the possible variations of each mineral. You may need to remind your class that when in the field, the best geologists can often do is to infer the identity of a mineral and that their inference is only as good as their observation of its properties.

Materials

For each student
- 1 science notebook
- 1 set of **12 Mineral Profile Sheets**
- 1 hand lens
- 1 pair of disposable gloves

For every two students

1   set of 12 minerals in an egg carton
1   cardboard tray

For the class

Class lists: "What We Know about Minerals" and "What We Want to Know about Minerals" (from Lesson 5)
1   pad of Post-it® notes, 76 × 127 mm (3 × 5 in)
1   sheet of newsprint, 60 × 90 mm (24 × 36 in)
1   colored marker

Preparation

1. Post the class lists in a visible place.

2. Draw a large circle on the newsprint and label it "Minerals." This is the second part of the Venn diagram that was started in Lesson 4. Post the new circle in a prominent place in the classroom.

3. Arrange materials in the materials center.

Procedure

1. Ask students to review their 12 mineral profile sheets and, with their partners, to identify the properties that best describe each mineral. Use questions such as the following to help focus the review:

   ■ How could you describe each mineral so that someone else could pick it out of a collection of minerals?

   ■ Are there some properties that are not helpful in describing the 12 minerals?

   ■ What properties are most useful in describing each of the 12 minerals?

2. Have one student from each pair go to the materials center and pick up two pairs of disposable gloves and a set of minerals that is different from the one the pair has used in previous lessons.

3. Invite a student to share a mineral's profile, one property at a time, while the rest of the class tries to pick out that mineral from their "new" set. Could the mineral be selected after only one property is described? After two properties? After three properties?

4. Ask students to comment on how their observations of their new set of minerals are different from, or the same as, the data they noted on their mineral profile sheets.

5. Have students group into teams of six and compare minerals. Encourage them to discuss how the three samples of each mineral are similar and different.

Final Activities

1. Ask students to suggest properties that all the minerals share. Record their ideas on Post-it® notes and place them inside the circle labeled "Minerals." In Lesson 16, you will use this circle and the one on rocks that students completed in Lesson 4 for a Venn diagram that compares rocks and minerals.

2. Return to the class lists entitled "What We Know about Minerals" and "What We Want to Know about Minerals," which students began in Lesson 5. Review each question. Place a check by those that have been answered. Identify questions that students still have and discuss how the questions might be answered.

Figure 13-1

Venn diagram circle for the properties of minerals

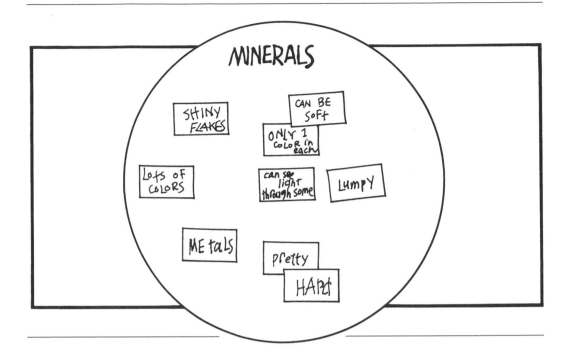

MINERALS

SHINY FLAKES

CAN BE SOFT

ONLY 1 COLOR in each

Lots of COLORS

can see light through some

LUMPY

METALS

Pretty

HARD

Assessment

The activities in Lessons 13 and 14 provide an opportunity to assess students' understanding of the properties of minerals. When listening to small group and class discussions describing minerals, note the following:

■ Which properties that they suggest are useful in identifying the mineral?

■ How many unnecessary or irrelevant properties do they suggest?

■ Which necessary or conclusive properties do they omit?

■ Do students refer to their profile sheets when they describe the properties of the minerals?

■ How closely do the students' descriptions correspond with the observations they have recorded on the mineral profile sheets

■ Do students observe the minerals again with the hand lens?

■ When students are comparing samples of the same mineral, do they

　■ Refer to the profile sheets?

　■ Propose testing again to clarify and resolve disagreements?

　■ Independently carry out proposed tests?

　■ Summarize or generalize observations?

■ Are students able to describe similarities that support their conclusion that two or more samples are in fact the same mineral?

■ How do students describe differences among samples of the same mineral?

■ When students identify the minerals in Lesson 14, note the following:

　■ Do they refer to reading selections in their Student Activity Books?

　■ Do they compare the mineral with its description?

　■ Do they use different properties to identify the minerals?

■ How well do the properties students use differentiate between similar minerals?

Identifying the Minerals

Overview and Objectives

In this lesson, students are introduced to the way geologists compare written information from a field guide with their own observations and field-test results to identify minerals. By comparing and contrasting the observations they have recorded on their mineral profile sheets with data on a field-guide card, students use deductive reasoning to identify each of the 12 minerals by name. They will again apply this process, as well as the observation and testing skills they have acquired during earlier lessons, in Lesson 15, where they are challenged to identify three "mystery minerals."

- Students analyze a mineral identification card and select the properties that will allow them to identify a sample of that mineral from among the 12 minerals in their set.

- Students apply problem-solving skills to identify each of the 12 minerals by name.

- Students make field guides with their set of mineral profile sheets.

Background

When geologists collect mineral samples, they attempt to identify and classify them by performing the same field tests that students have learned in this unit. The geologists compare the results of their tests with information from a **field guide,** a reference book that presents information about the properties of rocks and minerals in an organized way. When the geologists return to their laboratories, they perform more sophisticated tests to determine whether the conclusions they reached in the field were complete and accurate. Because many minerals have similar profiles, it is difficult to make a conclusive identification on the basis of field tests alone.

Many different field guides have been published. Some are simple and designed for the layperson; others are technical. Field guides are organized in different ways. Some use physical properties, such as shape and color, as the organizing principle; others use chemical structure. Both types provide a systematic presentation of information that enables the reader to use deductive reasoning to identify an unknown mineral sample. The information on the mineral identification cards, or field-guide cards, that students will use in this lesson was specially prepared for this purpose by a geologist.

The terms your students have used to record data on their mineral profile sheets will probably be different from those on the mineral identification cards. They may have chosen different words or looked at the minerals from a different perspective. Moreover, various samples of the same mineral can appear quite different. Many students will find that identification becomes easier after they have observed many samples.

Identification of the minerals is not a major goal of this lesson. Rather, the focus is the processes students use and their discussions of similarities and differences among the samples. Use your own knowledge of your students to determine when to provide additional clues or to invite pairs of students to share their success.

Materials

For each student
- 1   science notebook
- 1   set of 12 **Mineral Profile Sheets**
- 1   hand lens
- 1   set of 12 **Mineral Identification Cards** (blackline master)
- 1   pair of disposable gloves

For every two students
- 1   set of 12 minerals in an egg carton
- 1   cardboard tray
-     Glue or clear tape

Preparation

1. Make a sufficient number of copies of the blackline master **Mineral Identification Cards** (pgs. 111–13) so that each student will have a full set of 12 cards. Cut the sheets apart so that each card contains information on only one mineral.

Management Tip: In the first part of the lesson, students will continue working in pairs. You will give each pair one set of 12 cards for this purpose. After students have identified the minerals, you will give a second set of 12 mineral identification cards to each pair of students. Each child will then glue or tape a card to the back of the matching mineral profile sheet to create a "Minerals Field Guide."

2. Share the Bibliography with your school librarian. The students will consult these resources for the reports on minerals that you will assign at the end of this lesson. Find out how many of the materials in the Bibliography are available and whether the librarian can suggest additional resources.

3. Prepare the supplies for distribution.

Management Tip: When planning this lesson, note that students will need approximately 30 minutes to identify their minerals (**Procedure,** Step 3). Be sure to allocate enough time for this activity.

Procedure

1. Let students know that they now will receive some new information that will help them identify their 12 minerals by name. Distribute a set of mineral identification cards to each pair.

2. Review the type of information the cards contain. Explain to students that a geologist prepared these cards for them. Ask students to compare the information on the cards with the type of data they have recorded on their mineral profile sheets. How is the information different? How is it similar? Which words are exactly the same? Which words have the same meaning?

Figure 14-1

Identifying the minerals by name

3. Now challenge students to use all the information they have to match each of the cards to the mineral it describes.

    Note: Some students may find it helpful to identify the minerals by the process of elimination—by placing each mineral on top of the card that best describes it, beginning with the mineral whose identity is most certain. Other students will establish different strategies.

4. Discuss the results of this activity, starting with mineral A. If students suggest two or more names, ask them to explain their reasoning. Encourage students to justify their decisions with properties that "match" the mineral before they suggest its name.

5. Ask students to write the name of the appropriate mineral at the top of its "Mineral Profile Sheet."

6. Have students return their minerals, trays, and hand lenses to the materials center. Ask students to throw away their gloves and wash their hands.

Final Activities

1. Distribute a second set of mineral identification cards to each pair. Allow time for the students to glue or tape each card to the back of the corresponding mineral profile sheet. Encourage students to make covers for the booklet and then to staple everything together to create their field guides.

2. Ask students to think about how these minerals might be used. Let them know they each get to select one mineral or rock they have explored to research for an oral report. The reports should focus on how the rock or mineral is used. They will present these reports during Lesson 16.

   Note: Many students will approach this task more positively if they can choose their own rocks or minerals. Encourage the class to select as many different ones as possible, but do not insist that all the rocks and minerals be chosen. Students may explore the remaining rocks or minerals as an extension.

3. Using procedures you have established for doing research, review with students where they may find additional information for their reports.

   Management Tip: You may want to use other methods or materials available at your school to bind the students' "Minerals Field Guides."

Figure 14-2

Making the "Minerals Field Guides"

FELDSPAR

Feel:	Rough
Color:	Milky white, pinkish brown, or light greenish gray
Streak:	White
Hardness:	Medium to hard; barely scratched by nail (may also scratch nail)
Light:	No light shines through
Luster:	Glassy
Shape:	No special shape, flat sides

GALENA

Feel:	Smooth
Color:	Gray, silver
Streak:	Gray
Hardness:	Soft; scratched by penny
Light:	No light shines through
Luster:	Metallic
Shape:	Cube

CALCITE

Feel:	Smooth on sides
Color:	Clear
Streak:	White or gray
Hardness:	Soft to medium; barely scratched by penny (also scratches penny)
Light:	A lot of light shines through
Luster:	Glassy
Shape:	Crystal may look like a box that has been bent over

FLUORITE

Feel:	Smooth
Color:	Blue, green, yellow, purple
Streak:	White or pale
Hardness:	Medium; scratched by nail
Light:	A little light shines through
Luster:	Glassy
Shape:	Cube

GRAPHITE

Feel: Rough
Color: Silver black
Streak: Black
Hardness: Soft; scratched by penny
Light: No light shines through
Luster: Metallic; sometimes dull or greasy
Shape: No special shape

GYPSUM (ALABASTER)

Feel: Rough; often crumbling at edges
Color: White or light pink, gray, or brown
Streak: White or pale
Hardness: Soft; scratched by penny
Light: A little light shines through
Luster: Waxy, pearly
Shape: No special shape

HEMATITE

Feel: Rough
Color: Black or red
Streak: Gray, black, or reddish brown
Hardness: Medium; scratched by nail
Light: No light shines through
Luster: Metallic or dull
Shape: No special shape

MAGNETITE

Feel: Rough
Color: Black
Streak: Black or gray
Hardness: Medium; scratched by nail
Light: No light shines through
Luster: Metallic
Shape: No special shape

QUARTZ

Feel: Smooth
Color: Clear, white, green, pink, gray, yellow, brown, or red
Streak: White
Hardness: Hard; no scratch
Light: A lot of light shines through
Luster: Glassy
Shape: Six-sided crystal or a crystalline mass

Mineral Identification Card

TALC

Feel: Soft; like powder
Color: Light to medium gray
Streak: White
Hardness: Very soft; scratched by penny
Light: No light shines through
Luster: Pearly, waxy
Shape: No special shape

Mineral Identification Card

MUSCOVITE

Feel: Smooth, slippery
Color: Clear to yellow or pale brown
Streak: White or pale
Hardness: Soft; scratched by penny
Light: A lot of light shines through in thin places
Luster: Glassy
Shape: Thin, flat layers

Mineral Identification Card

SULFUR

Feel: Parts smooth and parts rough; crumbly
Color: Yellow
Streak: White
Hardness: Soft; scratched by penny
Light: No light shines through
Luster: Waxy
Shape: Masses not fully crystallized, some crystals

Mineral Identification Card

Exploring New Minerals

Overview and Objectives

This lesson provides an opportunity to assess students' knowledge of minerals and their skills in observing, describing, and summarizing properties. Students first decide which of the field tests from Lessons 7 to 11 will produce information that will be most helpful in identifying three mystery minerals. They then have an opportunity to perform these tests and to record the results. Finally, using their "Minerals Field Guides" and the problem-solving skills learned in preceding lessons, students determine which of their known minerals are most similar to each of the mystery minerals.

- Students apply tests to describe new minerals.

- Students record and discuss the results of their tests.

- Students identify and discuss similarities and differences between known and unknown minerals.

- Students use information they have recorded to identify three new minerals by name.

- Students communicate in writing how they identified the new minerals.

Background

The three mystery minerals that students will explore in this lesson are quartz, hematite, and biotite. The colors of the quartz and hematite samples are different from those of the samples in their sets of 12 minerals, and the shape of the quartz is different as well. The biotite is a new mineral that the students have not seen in this unit. The students' challenge is to observe the mystery minerals, to perform the tests that they believe would be most helpful in discovering more about the minerals' properties, and to try to identify the minerals.

Among the distinguishing properties of **quartz** are its hexagonal crystal shape and its hardness. Pure quartz is colorless; like some other minerals, however, quartz is found in different colors. These colors are due to impurities. An **impurity** is any substance in a mineral that is not part of its identifying chemical composition. Impurities do not change the mineral's crystal structure. Among the forms of quartz that contain specific impurities are citrine and amethyst, which are valued as gemstones. The rose quartz students examine in this lesson seldom forms as a fully developed six-sided crystal, but it still has the internal crystalline structure of quartz.

The color of **hematite** ranges from metallic gray to earthy red, depending on the presence of different impurities. Hematite's reddish-brown streak, texture, and lumpy form are its distinctive properties.

Biotite is a mica, as is muscovite. Minerals in the mica family are composed of thin, flaky sheets that are easily separated. Biotite and muscovite have the same crystal structure and many of the same properties. Both are flexible and flat and have a glassy luster. They are composed of many of the same chemical elements. Biotite is brown because it contains iron. Muscovite is clear to gray because it contains aluminum but no iron.

Materials

For each student

1 science notebook
1 "Minerals Field Guide"
1 set of 3 **Mineral Profile Sheets** (blackline master)
1 **Mineral Identification Card** for biotite (blackline master)
1 hand lens
1 pair of disposable gloves

For every two students

1 set of 12 minerals in an egg carton
3 mystery minerals: quartz (P), hematite (Q), biotite (R)
1 cardboard tray
1 magnet
1 plastic cup, 90 ml (3 oz)
1 dropper
1 steel nail
1 copper penny
1 white streak plate
1 black streak plate
1 penlight
Glue or tape

For the class

Venn diagram circle labeled "Minerals" (from Lesson 13)
1 pad of Post-it® notes, 76 × 127 mm (3 × 5 in)
Water, dish detergent, and paper towels

Preparation

1. Pour water into each cup until it is about one-half full.

2. Organize supplies in the materials center so that students can easily select the materials they need for the tests they choose to do.

3. Make three copies of the **Mineral Profile Sheet** (pg. 120) for each student. Make enough copies of the **Mineral Identification Card** for biotite (pg. 121) so that each student can have one copy. You will use the four cards on pg. 122 only if you do the **Extension** (pg. 119).

Management Tip: When planning this lesson, note that students will require about 20 minutes to test their three mystery minerals (**Procedure,** Step 9). Be sure to allow enough time for this activity.

4. Post the Venn diagram circle labeled "Minerals" in a visible location.

5. Arrange the supplies in the materials center.

Procedure

1. Ask students to share what they learned in Lesson 14 when they compared the information on their mineral profile sheets with the information on the mineral identification cards.

   ■ How was their information different from that of the geologist?

   ■ Which properties did they describe that the geologist did not?

   ■ What information did the geologist's mineral identification card have for each mineral that the students' profile sheet did not?

2. Ask students to think about each sample of galena that they observed in Lesson 13. What was the same about the samples? What was different? Encourage students to explain their answers.

3. Repeat the questions in Step 2 for fluorite and sulfur. How many different samples of a mineral do students think a geologist examines before she or he can identify it?

4. Let students know that they now will become amateur geologists. Their job will be to gather enough information, or clues, to identify three "mystery minerals."

5. Distribute three mineral profile sheets to each student. Ask them to label the sheets for minerals P, Q, and R in the first box after the word "Mineral."

6. Review the test supplies that are available for students' use in the materials center.

7. Ask one student from each pair to collect a set of minerals, a sample of each of the three mystery minerals, a cardboard tray, two pairs of disposable gloves, and two hand lenses from the materials center.

8. Challenge the students to decide which tests they will use to identify the mystery minerals.

9. Allow about 20 minutes for students to observe, test, and record the properties of the three mystery minerals on their mineral profile sheets.

10. Invite students to share with the class what they learned about each of the three minerals.

11. Now ask students to compare mystery mineral P with the 12 minerals in their egg carton. Remind them to review the information they have recorded in their "Minerals Field Guides." Use questions such as the following:

    ■ Which minerals in their set are similar to mineral P?

    ■ Which properties do they share?

    ■ In what ways are the minerals that are similar also different?

12. Repeat Step 11 with minerals Q and R.

13. Ask students to compare the properties of the 3 mystery minerals with the properties of their 12 known minerals. Challenge them to discover whether any of the mystery minerals are in fact ones they have already studied.

14. Ask students to share their conclusions. What properties did each mineral have that led to this conclusion? What properties did the minerals not have?

15. Make sure students realize that two of the minerals are the same as those in their sets. Clarify any confusion by emphasizing similarities and differences among mineral samples.

Figure 15-1

Exploring the
mystery minerals

16. Let the students know that the name of mineral R is biotite. Biotite, like muscovite, is a member of the mica family. The micas are composed of thin, flaky sheets that are easily separated. Give each student a mineral identification card for biotite.

17. Have students clean up their work areas and return their supplies to the materials center. Remind them to throw away their gloves and wash their hands.

Final Activities

1. Ask students to write several sentences in their science notebooks about the following:

   ■ How did you go about trying to identify the properties of the mystery minerals?

   ■ What properties made you think each mineral was, or was not, one of those in your mineral set?

2. Referring to the Venn diagram started in Lesson 13, ask students to think about the properties posted in the circle labeled "Minerals."

   ■ Should any properties be removed?

   ■ Should any properties be added?

   ■ Should any properties be placed outside the circle? (In other words, are there any properties that students did not observe in any of the minerals?)

   Record students' new ideas on Post-it® notes and place them in the circle.

3. Give students time to glue or tape the biotite card to Mineral Profile Sheet R and to add it to their "Minerals Field Guide." Students also may insert the new profile sheets for quartz (mineral P) and hematite (mineral Q) in their "Minerals Field Guide" with the other profile sheets for these minerals.

4. Remind students that they will present oral reports on minerals and rocks during Lesson 16. Ask them whether they have any questions about the reports.

Extension

SCIENCE

Invite students to perform the field tests on halite (mineral M), satin spar gypsum (mineral N), "desert rose" selenite (mineral O), and clear selenite (mineral S), the new minerals they observed in Lesson 12 when they studied crystal shapes. Make four new copies of the mineral profile sheets for each student and have the test materials available. Ask students to perform the tests, record their observations on the mineral profile sheets, and add the four new pages to their "Minerals Field Guide." The blackline master for the mineral profile sheet is found on pg. 120 of this lesson; blackline masters for the four mineral identification cards are on pg. 122.

Note: This extension is also suggested as an additional assessment (see pg. 146). If you wish to use it at the end of the unit, do not use it at this time.

Assessment

This lesson requires students to apply skills and concepts learned over the past eight lessons. Use the following questions to help guide your observations and document growth and learning:

■ Do students work cooperatively to choose tests that provide useful information?

■ Do students compare the new minerals with their set of 12 minerals?

■ Are students able to organize and apply tests independently?

■ Do students obtain and record reasonable results?

■ Do students compare results with information in their "Minerals Field Guides"?

■ Are students able to defend their conclusions with information from their tests, "Minerals Field Guides," or reading selections?

Name: _____

Date: _____

Mineral Profile Sheet

Mineral ▢	Feel
	Smell
Streak color	**Luster**
Light	**Magnetism**
Hardness	**Shape**

BIOTITE

Feel:	Smooth
Color:	Black or dark brown
Streak:	White or light brown
Hardness:	Soft; scratched by penny
Light:	Some light shines through in places
Luster:	Shiny
Shape:	Thin, flat layers

Mineral Identification Card

BIOTITE

Feel:	Smooth
Color:	Black or dark brown
Streak:	White or light brown
Hardness:	Soft; scratched by penny
Light:	Some light shines through in places
Luster:	Shiny
Shape:	Thin, flat layers

Mineral Identification Card

BIOTITE

Feel:	Smooth
Color:	Black or dark brown
Streak:	White or light brown
Hardness:	Soft; scratched by penny
Light:	Some light shines through in places
Luster:	Shiny
Shape:	Thin, flat layers

Mineral Identification Card

BIOTITE

Feel:	Smooth
Color:	Black or dark brown
Streak:	White or light brown
Hardness:	Soft; scratched by penny
Light:	Some light shines through in places
Luster:	Shiny
Shape:	Thin, flat layers

Mineral Identification Card

GYPSUM (CLEAR SELENITE CRYSTAL)

Feel: Smooth
Color: Clear
Streak: White
Hardness: Soft; scratched by penny
Light: A lot of light shines through
Luster: Glassy
Shape: No special shape

HALITE

Feel: Smooth
Color: Clear or white
Streak: Gray
Hardness: Soft; scratched by penny
Light: A lot of light shines through
Luster: Glassy
Shape: Cube

GYPSUM (BLADED SELENITE CRYSTAL AGGREGATE)

Feel: Rough; sharp, rounded edges
Color: Light brown and white
Streak: White
Hardness: Soft; scratched by penny
Light: A little light shines through
Luster: Dull to waxy; small, shiny crystals in some places
Shape: Looks like a flower

GYPSUM (SATIN SPAR VARIETY)

Feel: Rough
Color: White with traces of pink, red, or brown
Streak: White
Hardness: Soft; scratched by penny
Light: A little light shines through
Luster: Waxy; lines of shiny crystals in places
Shape: No special shape

How Are Rocks and Minerals Used?

Overview and Objectives

Students have now explored the physical properties of 12 rocks and 16 minerals. This lesson focuses on how rocks and minerals are used. As students read about rocks and minerals and listen to and discuss their classmates' reports, they gain new information about rocks and minerals and broaden their understanding of the relationship between them. Finally, students apply this understanding to complete a Venn diagram that shows the similarities and differences between rocks and minerals.

- Students suggest possible uses for rocks and minerals.

- Students read to learn more about how rocks and minerals are used.

- Students prepare and share reports on specific rocks and minerals.

- Students complete a Venn diagram showing the similarities and differences between the rocks and minerals they have studied.

Background

As far back as 2.5 million years ago, our ancestors used rocks that lay on the earth's surface to make tools. Today, rocks on and below the earth's surface provide the raw materials needed to construct buildings and manufacture a wide range of tools and everyday objects.

Many students are unaware that they use items made from rocks and minerals daily. This is probably because the manufactured items usually do not resemble rocks. Anything that is not a direct animal or plant product is probably made from rocks or from the minerals found in rocks. As geologists sometimes say, "If it's not grown, it's mined!"

It would be impossible to construct buildings without rocks. Basalt, granite, gneiss, marble, and sandstone have been used for centuries as building stones and for monuments and decorations. We use limestone and conglomerate to make the foundations of buildings. Bricks, plaster, and glass are made from rocks.

Other uses of rocks are less obvious. For example, we use pumice as an abrasive for cleaning and limestone in manufacturing carpet. Phosphate rock is a major ingredient in fertilizers. We use cinder and conglomerate to build roads. Plastics are made from petroleum, which is extracted from rocks.

Finally, as students learned in Lesson 4, minerals are found in rocks. Some rocks contain large quantities of commercially valuable minerals, such as gold and diamonds.

The science of mineralogy has changed over time. Originally, geologists concentrated on identifying minerals. Later, they began to focus on what minerals can reveal about the history of the earth and how they can be used. By examining rocks, which are made of minerals, scientists can learn about the pressure under which the minerals grew, changes in the temperature of the earth, the composition of meteorites, and even changes in the intensity of the earth's magnetic field.

New technologies have made it possible for scientists to duplicate minerals in the laboratory. Synthetic minerals are used for jewelry as well as industrial purposes. Synthetic quartz crystals and diamonds, for example, are now used extensively in industry. Overall, natural minerals are used in far greater quantities than synthetic minerals.

Minerals are the source of many metals. Any mineral that contains metal in large enough amounts to be worth mining is called an ore. Mineral ores are the source of metals such as iron, copper, aluminum, zinc, and mercury. Minerals and their byproducts are used for a wide range of industrial purposes. Students will probably be surprised to learn that minerals can be found in almost every aspect of their environment.

The following are common uses for the minerals included in this unit:

A. Feldspar: Ceramics (both porcelain and glazes), medicines such as Kaopectate™ (from kaolin, a weathered form of feldspar), household abrasive cleaners, glassmaking

B. Quartz: Radios, watches, computers, jewelry, glass, abrasives, optics

C. Galena: Source of lead, used in batteries, paints, radiation shields, electronic components, ammunition

D. Calcite: Fertilizer, medicine, cement

E. Fluorite: Enamel, optics, steel manufacturing, toothpaste

F. Graphite: Lubricant, electrodes, pencils, high-temperature tools, batteries, sports equipment

G. Hematite: Source of iron ore, paint pigment (red ocher)

H. Gypsum: Plaster (orthopedic casts, drywall), fertilizer, furnace and stove linings, sculpture (only from alabaster), cement, baked goods

I. Magnetite: Source of iron ore

J. Muscovite: Electric insulators, furnace and stove windows

K. Sulfur: Medicines, gunpowder, fireworks, fungicides, matches, fertilizer

L. Talc: Baby powder, hand lotion, lipstick, paint, paper

M. Halite: Salt, food additive, deicing agent; as sodium hydroxide, used in paper, soap, and petroleum manufacture

N. Gypsum (satin spar): See H

O. Gypsum (bladed selenite crystal aggregate): See H

P. Quartz: See B

Q. Hematite: See G

R. Biotite: No current commercial uses; once used for heat-resistant windows in ovens and furnaces

S. Gypsum (clear selenite crystal): See H

Materials

For each student

1   science notebook

1   copy of Record Sheet 1-A: Rocks—Record of My Observations or **4-A: Minerals—Record of My Observations**

1   "Minerals Field Guide"

1   hand lens

1   pair of disposable gloves

For every two students

5   different samples of 1 of the rocks or minerals studied in this unit

1   cardboard tray

For the class

Copies of **Rock Information Cards** (blackline master on pgs. 132–37)

Class lists "What We Know about Rocks" and "What We Want to Know about Rocks" (from Lesson 1)

Class lists "What We Know about Minerals" and "What We Want to Know about Minerals" (from Lesson 5)

Class list "Rocks and Minerals and How We Use Them"

Venn diagram circles labeled "Rocks" and "Minerals" (from Lessons 4 and 13, respectively)

1   pad of Post-it® notes, 76 × 127 (3 × 5 in)

1   sheet of newsprint, 60 × 90 cm (24 × 36 in)

Colored markers

Optional: Children's resource books on rocks and minerals (see Bibliography)

Preparation

1. Prepare the blackline master **Rock Information Cards** (pgs. 132–37) as needed for students. You may want to copy extra cards for students who wish to study more than one rock.

2. Set up the materials center with the rocks, minerals, trays, gloves, and hand lenses.

3. Decide how the students will prepare and present their reports on rocks and minerals. The reports should include information from the students' science notebooks, record sheets, "Minerals Field Guides," the reading selections, the rock information cards, and additional resource books. You may wish to have students do the reading and reporting during language arts time.

4. Post the Venn diagram circles labeled "Rocks" and "Minerals" in a prominent position.

Procedure

1. Review your classroom process for preparing oral reports. Then draw students' attention to the resources they may use for this activity. These include their science notebooks, the reading selections, and the rock information cards.

2. Ask a student from each pair to go to the materials center, put on a pair of disposable gloves, and pick up at least five samples of the rock or mineral they have chosen for their report, a cardboard tray, another pair of disposable gloves, and two hand lenses. Distribute the rock information cards as needed.

3. Allow time for students to do their research, organize their information, and prepare their reports.

4. Have the students return their five rock or mineral samples to the materials center. Allow them a few final minutes to complete their report preparation while you reassemble the rocks and minerals into sets of 12. Then have each pair pick up a complete set of rocks and minerals.

5. Have students present their oral reports. Encourage other students to examine the sample being discussed. Afterwards, encourage them to ask questions.

6. Have students return their rocks and minerals, trays, and hand lenses to the materials center. Remind students to throw away their gloves and wash their hands.

Figure 16-1

Reporting on how rocks and minerals are used

Final Activities

1. Referring to the class lists from Lesson 1, ask students to help you place a check by questions that have been answered and add any new questions students have. Repeat this process for the class lists on minerals from Lesson 5.

2. Draw students' attention to the Venn diagram circle labeled "Rocks." Ask students to state new properties and uses for rocks. Record their responses on Post-it® notes and place them inside the circle. Ask whether any of the notes should be removed.

3. Repeat Step 2 with the "Minerals" circle of the Venn diagram.

4. Move the "Rocks" circle so that it overlaps the "Minerals" circle. With a marker, redraw the portion of the circle that is covered, as shown in Figure 16–2.

5. Challenge students to look for properties and descriptions that are the same in both circles. Move the notes that list these properties into the area where the circles overlap.

6. Ask students to write several sentences in their science notebooks about how minerals and rocks are different and how they are the same.

Figure 16-2

Completed Venn diagram

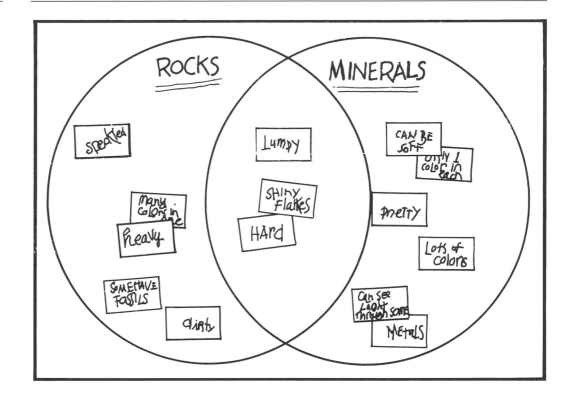

Extensions

SOCIAL STUDIES

1. Encourage students to do additional research on the rocks used to build monuments such as the Lincoln Memorial and Washington Monument in Washington, D.C., or well-known buildings in their area. Where did the rocks come from? How were they transported? How were the buildings constructed?

SCIENCE

2. Invite a geologist or a member of a rock club to bring in a collection of local rocks. Encourage students to compare these samples with the rocks they have been studying.

SCIENCE

3. Give each student three note cards and short strips of tape. Have them write "P" for "plant" on one card, "A" for "animal" on the second, and "R" or "M," for "rock" or "mineral," on the third. Ask the students to look around the room and to find one object in the room that was made from a rock or mineral, one from a plant, and one from an animal. Then ask them to identify each of these objects by taping the appropriate card to it. Encourage them to tape the card to the specific part of the object that they have identified (for example, a metal screw in a chair).

Note: Many children think of toys as real animals. They may want to label stuffed animals with the "A" card. Be prepared to help them work through this issue.

Figure 16-3

*Students labeling
classroom items*

Assessment

The students' oral reports provide information about their skills in organizing and interpreting information. Listen for evidence that they have applied the following concepts and skills:

Concepts

- The properties of rocks reflect the way they were formed and the minerals in them.

- The properties of rocks and minerals determine how they are used.

Skills

- Using senses to identify properties.

- Comparing similarities and differences on the basis of observable properties.

- Performing tests and interpreting results.

- Reading for more information.

- Communicating through discussion.

The students' suggestions for the Venn diagram provide an opportunity to assess growth in their knowledge and ideas about how rocks and minerals are the same and different. Ideas to check for include the following:

- There are many different types of rocks.

- Rocks are formed in different ways and change over time.

- Rocks have several different materials in them.

- Different minerals can have the same physical properties.

The post-unit and additional assessments provide further opportunities for your students to share what they have learned and for you to evaluate their growth.

Post-Unit Assessment

The post-unit assessment on pgs. 139–40 is a matched follow-up to the pre-unit assessments in Lessons 1 and 5. By comparing students' pre- and post-unit responses, you will be able to document their growth in knowledge about rocks and minerals.

Additional Assessments

Additional assessments for this unit are provided on pgs. 143–49. They include a student self-assessment and three other assessments that you may wish to perform.

Basalt

Basalt is the most common volcanic rock in the world. It often is made up of lava that has cooled and hardened. Sometimes entire islands are formed from volcanic rock. You can see basalt on the slopes of old volcanoes in the state of New Jersey.

Basalt is usually black or gray-black. Although basalt is a volcanic rock, it is not shiny like obsidian, and it is not light like pumice. Basalt is hard and dense. Its texture is fine.

Basalt is a source of iron ore and copper. The basalt in the area around Lake Superior in Canada has large copper deposits. Beautiful dark-blue sapphires, used for jewelry, are among the valuable minerals found in basalt. If you were born in September, the sapphire is your birthstone!

Basalt is one of the strongest and most durable of all rocks. Because of this, it is used for the outside of buildings, for roads, and for tombstones.

Rock Information Card   STC/*Rocks and Minerals*

Conglomerate

Conglomerate is found all over the world. It is a sedimentary rock that forms from small pieces of other rocks that become pressed together at the bottom of a lake or an ocean.

Sometimes conglomerate contains pebbles of older rocks and looks like a chocolate chip cookie! Other times, conglomerate has tiny pieces and looks like a chunk of concrete. The pebbles in conglomerate are usually round and smooth. Sometimes they look polished. This is because they have been worn down by wind, rain, ice, or snow.

Conglomerate is often softer than other rocks. It can wear down easily. Because of this, it is not used by itself to make buildings. Conglomerate is used in concrete building foundations.

Rock Information Card   STC/*Rocks and Minerals*

Gneiss

Gneiss (pronounced "nice") is a hard, coarse metamorphic rock. It is formed when shale and granite are heated and pressed together under the surface of the earth. Gneiss and granite can look alike, even to rock experts. As a joke, they often warn, "Don't take gneiss for granite!"

There are many different kinds of gneiss. Its color may be dark or light. Gneiss often has bands, or layers, that are formed when its minerals flatten under heat and pressure.

Gneiss is found all over the world. It can be seen in mountain ranges such as the Alps in Switzerland, the Andes in South America, and the Rocky Mountains in the western United States.

Polished gneiss is used for the fronts of buildings. It is considered one of the most beautiful rocks in the world. Some gneiss contains garnets, dark-red minerals that look like rubies.

Rock Information Card   STC/*Rocks and Minerals*

Granite

Granite is one of the hardest of all rocks. For this reason, some people call it the "rock everlasting." Granite is the most common rock in the earth's crust. It is an igneous rock, formed when molten rock cools underground.

Granite is usually light in color. It may be speckled or banded. Its crystals may be large and easy to see. Can you see crystals in your granite? What minerals do you think they could be?

Granite is found in high mountains like the Rockies. It is also found in older, smaller mountains like the Appalachians. Granite is common in the eastern United States; in fact, New Hampshire is called "The Granite State." In some places in England, granite blocks as large as houses cover the hillsides. These huge rocks are called "tors."

Granite is used for buildings, monuments, bridges, and curbstones. Tin and copper are mined from granite.

Rock Information Card   STC/*Rocks and Minerals*

Limestone

Limestone is not green and has nothing to do with a fruit! Its name comes from a Latin word that means "mud" and an old English word for "glue."

Limestone is a sedimentary rock. It may be white, gray, or yellowish. Rain and wind can wear it down, making it look rounded.

Fossils are often found in limestone. Some types of limestone are formed from the shells of sea animals. Coral reefs, or fossil reefs, are made up of many thousands of these tiny creatures.

Limestone is used to make cement and glass. It is an ingredient in agricultural lime, which farmers put on soil. Limestone is also used for building materials. Chalk is a form of pure limestone. Gas and petroleum may be found in large limestone deposits.

Limestone was once used in buildings. What do you suppose has happened to some of those buildings?

Rock Information Card   STC/*Rocks and Minerals*

Marble

Marble is a beautiful, very hard metamorphic rock that is formed from limestone. Because it contains thousands of sparkling crystals, marble is sometimes called the "shining stone."

Sculptors use pure white marble, which is rare and expensive. Many of the famous statues of the Italian artist Michelangelo, who lived in the 1600s, are made of white marble. Marble is often streaked with green, rose, or pink. Some marble is even black.

Marble has been used for centuries on the floors, walls, and ceilings of churches and important buildings. The Romans used marble to build their temples.

One of the world's most famous marbles, which is called "Carrara," comes from Italy. In the United States, marble is found in the Adirondack Mountains in New York State and in the Sierra Nevada Mountains in the West. Marble is cut in large blocks from quarries, which are large pits in the earth that have been dug out by miners.

Rock Information Card   STC/*Rocks and Minerals*

Obsidian

Obsidian is sometimes called "natural glass" or "volcanic glass." It is a black, shiny rock that forms when lava erupts from a volcano and quickly cools.

Because obsidian cools very quickly, its crystals are usually very small. Snowflake obsidian, however, is a rare form of the rock that is dotted with large white crystals.

Obsidian got its name from a man who found this rock in Ethiopia, which is in eastern Africa. It is found near volcanoes throughout the world. In the United States, obsidian has been found in Yellowstone National Park in Wyoming.

Obsidian is one of the first materials known to be used in trade among ancient peoples. They used it to make weapons and tools. Knives made of obsidian were used to cut meat.

Can you find obsidian in your set of rocks?

Rock Information Card   STC/*Rocks and Minerals*

Pumice

Pumice is a volcanic rock. Its surface is covered by tiny holes. These holes were made by gases that bubbled out when the lava erupted from a volcano.

Some pumice is so light that it will float in water! According to one story, sailors walked two miles to shore on floating pumice after a volcanic explosion on an island in the Pacific Ocean. Because it is so light, pumice is often used on movie sets. When you see Superman pick up a heavy boulder, it's probably made of pumice!

Around the house, you may use pumice for polishing or cleaning. It's also used in sandpaper. And if you get a callus on your foot, you can smooth it down with a pumice stone. In industry, pumice is used to make heat and sound insulation materials.

Rock Information Card   STC/*Rocks and Minerals*

Sandstone

Sandstone is a sedimentary rock that sometimes looks like pieces of beach sand that have been glued together. The color and strength of sandstone vary. Some sandstones are soft, almost crumbly. The grains may be small, medium, or large. The edges may be rounded or sharp, depending on how much the rock has been weathered.

Red sandstone is common in the canyons and mountains of New Mexico, Utah, and Arizona. Members of ancient American civilizations such as the Anasazi built their homes into the sides of these canyons. If you walk to the bottom of Canyon de Chelly in Arizona, you can still see parts of these ancient homes.

When sandstone is squeezed by underground pressure, it forms quartzite. Quartzite contains quartz crystals. Sounds confusing, doesn't it? But by now you probably can explain the difference between quartz and quartzite. Which is a rock? Which is a mineral? Why?

Sandstone is found worldwide. It is used in building materials. It is also used to make . . . sandpaper!

Rock Information Card   STC/*Rocks and Minerals*

Schist

Schist is a metamorphic rock made from shale and mud. It can be brown, black, or dark green. You can see it when you are riding along a road that cuts through low mountains like the Blue Ridge in the eastern United States. It also is found along glaciers in Alaska.

Schist is broken up and used in making roads. It may have large crystals that can be used in jewelry. For example, garnets, a red gemstone, are often found in schist. Schist sometimes contains shiny flecks of biotite or muscovite.

Do you see minerals in your schist?

Rock Information Card   STC/*Rocks and Minerals*

Post-Unit Assessment

Overview

This post-unit assessment is matched to the pre-unit assessment in Lesson 1 and to the assessment questions about minerals in Lesson 5. By comparing individual responses from this activity with those from Lessons 1 and 5, you will be able to document each student's learning over the course of this unit. When students respond again to these questions and review the class lists, they may realize how much they have learned about rocks and minerals and about identifying and describing their properties.

Materials

For each student
  1   science notebook

For the class
  3   sheets of newsprint
      Colored markers
      Masking tape
      Class lists: "What We Know about Rocks" (from Lesson 1) and "What We Know about Minerals" (from Lesson 5)

Preparation

1. Label one sheet of newsprint with the words "What We Know about Rocks," one with "What We Know about Minerals," and a third with "Questions We Still Have." Date the sheets and post them in a prominent position in the classroom. You may need extra sheets of newsprint.

2. Have the class lists from Lessons 1 and 5 ready to display.

Procedure

1. Ask students to think about what they have learned in this unit. Have them write down what they now know about rocks and minerals. When you compare these entries with those from Lessons 1 and 5, look for new ideas as well as for indications that students' existing ideas have been refined.

2. Display the original class lists. Ask students to point out ideas they now know to be true. What experiences did they have during the unit that confirmed these statements?

3. Ask students to look at the lists again and to point to statements they would like to correct, improve, or delete. Again, ask them to support their suggestions with experiences from the unit.

4. Finally, ask students to share new information they gained from the unit. What else have they learned? What new questions do they have? Record their answers on the newly prepared newsprint. Point out that science involves asking questions and conducting investigations to find out the answers, and that the answers usually lead to more questions and additional investigations.

Additional Assessments

Overview

This section presents some suggestions for assessment activities. Although it is not essential to do all of the suggested assessments, it is recommended that students do Assessment 1.

■ **Assessment 1** is a questionnaire that students can use to evaluate themselves.

■ **Assessment 2** challenges students to perform the field tests on halite, gypsum satin spar, bladed selenite crystal aggregate, and clear selenite crystal, the four mineral specimens that they first explored in Lesson 12.

■ **Assessment 3** gives you an opportunity to meet with students individually and to assess their responses to questions concerning rocks and minerals.

■ **Assessment 4** gives you an opportunity to assess students' ability to share what they have learned about rocks and minerals with invited class visitors.

Assessment 1: Student Self-Assessment

Using a questionnaire, students assess their own learning and participation during this unit.

Materials

For each student
   1   **Student Self-Assessment** (on pgs. 144–45)

Procedure

   1.   Distribute a copy of the Student Self-Assessment to each student. Review it with the class. Explain to the students that it is important to stop from time to time and think about how they are working.

   2.   Allow students time to complete the self-assessment during class, or ask them to complete it as a homework assignment.

Rocks and Minerals
Student Self-Assessment

Name: _____

Date: _____

1. Write three things you now know about rocks.

2. Write three things you now know about minerals.

3. What questions do you still have about rocks and minerals?

4. List the activities that you liked best in *Rocks and Minerals.* Explain why you liked them.

Rocks and Minerals
Student Self-Assessment, *continued*   Name: _____

5. How well do you think you and your partner worked together? Give some examples.

6. Take another look at your "Minerals Field Guide." Describe how well you think you recorded your observations and test results.

7. How do you feel about learning science? Circle words that apply to you.

    a. Interested   b. Bored   c. Nervous   d. Excited

    e. Confused   f. Successful   g. Relaxed   h. Happy

    i. Now write down at least one word of your own. _____

Assessment 2: Testing Four Minerals

This activity may be used to assess students' process skills. Ask students to perform as many of the field tests on minerals M, N, O, and S as they wish and to record results on mineral profile sheets.

Note: This activity may also be used as an extension in Lesson 15.

Materials

For each student

4 **Mineral Profile Sheets** (blackline master, pg. 148)
4 **Mineral Identification Cards** (blackline master, pg. 149)
1 hand lens
1 pair of disposable gloves
Crayons or colored pencils

For each pair of students

1 sample of mineral M (halite)
1 sample of mineral N (gypsum, satin spar variety)
1 sample of mineral O (gypsum, bladed selenite crystal aggregate)
1 sample of mineral S (gypsum, clear selenite crystal)
1 cardboard tray
1 white streak plate
1 black streak plate
1 magnet
1 nail
1 penny
1 penlight

For the class

Water, dish detergent, and paper towels

Preparation

1. Make four copies of the blank mineral profile sheet (pg. 148) and a set of four mineral identification cards (pg. 149) for each student.

2. Set up the materials center.

Procedure

1. Distribute disposable gloves and samples of minerals M, N, O, and S to each student pair. Distribute four blank mineral profile sheets to each student. Ask them to write the letters M, N, O, or S after the word "Mineral" in the first box on the sheets.

2. Challenge students to find out as much as they can about each of these minerals by using any of the field tests they wish. Remind them to record all information in the corresponding spaces on the mineral profile sheets.

3. After the students have finished the tests, distribute the mineral identification cards for all four minerals. Have students attach the cards to the mineral profile sheets and add them to their "Minerals Field Guides."

4. Remind students to throw away their gloves and wash their hands.

Assessment 3: Individual Student Meetings

Meet with students individually. Record their responses to questions such as:

- How are rocks and minerals different?
- What minerals might you find in your home? Why?
- Which mineral or rock was your favorite? Why? Describe its properties.
- Suppose you found an interesting rock. How would you go about learning what kind of rock it is?

Assessment 4: Presentation to Visitors

Invite one or more visitors such as the principal, a geologist, parents, or children from another class to your room to listen to your students discuss rocks and minerals. Such a visit motivates many students to talk more about their work and to express feelings about the process skills and concepts they learned.

To help students prepare, let the class know who will visit. Ask them to spend a few minutes thinking about what they have learned during the *Rocks and Minerals* unit. Go around the room, asking each student to share one thing that he or she has learned. It is fine if some students give identical answers.

Date: _____

Mineral Profile Sheet

Mineral ☐	**Feel**
	Smell
Streak color	**Luster**
Light	**Magnetism**
Hardness	**Shape**

GYPSUM (CLEAR SELENITE CRYSTAL)

Feel: Smooth
Color: Clear
Streak: White
Hardness: Soft; scratched by penny
Light: A lot of light shines through
Luster: Glassy
Shape: No special shape

HALITE

Feel: Smooth
Color: Clear or white
Streak: Gray
Hardness: Soft; scratched by penny
Light: A lot of light shines through
Luster: Glassy
Shape: Cube

GYPSUM (BLADED SELENITE CRYSTAL AGGREGATE)

Feel: Rough; sharp, rounded edges
Color: Light brown and white
Streak: White
Hardness: Soft; scratched by penny
Light: A little light shines through
Luster: Dull to waxy; small, shiny crystals in some places
Shape: Looks like a flower

GYPSUM (SATIN SPAR VARIETY)

Feel: Rough
Color: White with traces of pink, red, or brown
Streak: White
Hardness: Soft; scratched by penny
Light: A little light shines through
Luster: Waxy; lines of shiny crystals in places
Shape: No special shape

Bibliography: Resources for Teachers and Students

This Bibliography provides a sampling of books that complement the unit. It is divided into the following categories:

- Resources for Teachers
- Resources for Students

These materials come well recommended. They have been favorably reviewed, and teachers have found them useful.

If a book goes out of print or if you seek additional titles, you may wish to consult the following resources:

Appraisal: Science Books for Young People (The Children's Science Book Review Committee, Boston).

Published quarterly, this periodical reviews new science books available for young people. Each book is reviewed by a librarian and by a scientist. The Children's Science Book Review Committee is sponsored by the Science Education Department of Boston University's School of Education and the New England Roundtable of Children's Librarians.

Gath, Tracy, and Maria Sosa, eds. *Science Books & Films' Best Books for Children, 1992–95*. Washington, DC: American Association for the Advancement of Science, 1996.

This volume, part of a continuing series, is a compilation of the most highly rated science books that have been reviewed recently in the periodical *Science Books & Films*.

National Science Resources Center. *Resources for Teaching Elementary School Science.* Washington, DC: National Academy Press, 1996.

This guide provides extensive information about some 350 hands-on, inquiry-centered science curriculum materials for grades K–6. It also annotates other published materials—books on teaching science, science book lists, and periodicals for teachers and students. The guide includes annotated listings of museums and federal and professional organizations throughout the country with programs and other resources to assist in the teaching of elementary school science.

Science and Children (National Science Teachers Association, Arlington, VA).

Each March, this monthly periodical provides an annotated bibliography of outstanding science trade books primarily for elementary students.

Science Books & Films (American Association for the Advancement of Science, Washington, DC).

Published nine times a year, this periodical offers critical reviews of a wide range of new science materials, from books to audiovisual materials to electronic resources. The reviews are primarily written by scientists and science educators. *Science Books & Films* is useful for librarians, media specialists, curriculum supervisors, science teachers, and others responsible for recommending and purchasing scientific materials.

Scientific American (Scientific American, Inc., New York).

Each December, this periodical compiles and reviews a selection of outstanding new science books for children.

Resources for Teachers

Bell, Pat, and David Wright. *Rocks and Minerals.* New York: Collier Books, 1985.

A field guide for adults. Describes common rocks and minerals. Contains color photographs of rocks and minerals, organized by family name.

Booth, Basil. *Rocks and Minerals.* Secaucus, NJ: Chartwell Books, 1993.

Briefly explains properties of minerals and rocks and the field tests used to identify these properties. Provides color photographs and descriptions of the properties of more than 125 common rocks and minerals.

Desautels, Paul E. *Gems in the Smithsonian.* Washington, DC: Smithsonian Institution Press, 1972.

Illustrated guide to minerals in the Smithsonian Collection.

Dishon, Dee, and Pat Wilson O'Leary. *A Guidebook for Cooperative Learning: Techniques for Creating More Effective Schools.* Holmes Beach, FL: Learning Publications, 1984.

A practical guide for teachers who are embarking on the implementation of cooperative-learning techniques in the classroom.

Hyler, Nelson W. *Rocks and Minerals.* Los Angeles: Price/Stern/Sloan, 1987.

A traditional field guide for adults, with details on the chemical composition and crystal structures of rocks and minerals.

Johnson, David W., Roger T. Johnson, and Edythe Johnson Holubec. *Circles of Learning: Cooperation in the Classroom.* Alexandria, VA: Association for Supervision and Curriculum Development, 1984.

Presents the case for cooperative learning in a concise and readable form. Reviews the research, outlines implementation strategies, and answers many questions.

Lambert, David. *Rocks and Minerals.* London: Franklin Watts, 1986.

A traditional field guide for adults.

Moody, Richard. *The Concise Illustrated Book of Rocks and Minerals.* London: Regency House Publishing, 1993.

A brief description of some rocks and minerals, where they are found, and common uses. Illustrated with photographs and photomicrographs showing crystal structures.

Resources for Students

Aliki. *Fossils Tell of Long Ago.* New York: HarperCollins Children's Books, 1972.

Written for elementary school children, this book explains how fossils are formed and what they tell us about the past.

Archer, Jules. *Earthquake!* New York: Macmillan Children's Book Group, 1991.

Examines the nature, origins, and dangers of earthquakes and discusses the warning systems that predict and detect them.

Asimov, Isaac. *How Did We Find Out about Coal?* New York: Walker and Company, 1980.

Presents a history of fire, considers wood as a fuel, and discusses the formation of coal and the history of its use as a fuel.

Bains, Rae. *Rocks and Minerals.* Mahwah, NJ: Troll Associates, 1985.

Discusses the characteristics and uses of some common rocks and minerals.

Booth, Basil. *Volcanoes and Earthquakes.* Englewood Cliffs, NJ: Silver Burdett Press, 1991.

Examines and explains the nature of volcanoes and earthquakes and the scientific methods used to predict their occurrence.

_____. *Earthquakes and Volcanoes.* New York: Macmillan Children's Book Group, 1992.

Discusses how to predict and survive earthquakes and volcanic eruptions.

Bramwell, Martyn. *Rocks and Fossils.* London: Usborne Publishing, 1983.

Overview of the families of rocks, minerals, and fossils. Includes experiments.

Brandt, Keith. *Caves.* Mahwah, NJ: Troll Associates, 1985.

Describes how caves are formed and what one might find inside.

Cole, Joanna. *The Magic School Bus: Inside the Earth.* New York: Scholastic, 1987.

On a field trip in the magic school bus, Ms. Frizzle's class learns firsthand about different kinds of rocks and the formation of the earth.

Dineen, Jacqueline. *Metals and Minerals.* Hillside, NJ: Enslow Publishers, 1988.

Explains how people search for minerals and how they are mined and put to use.

Fradin, Dennis Brindell. *Disaster! Volcanoes.* Chicago: Children's Press, 1982.

Describes the characteristics of volcanoes, why and how they erupt, and how eruptions are predicted.

Gans, Roma. *Rock Collecting.* New York: HarperCollins Children's Books, 1984.

> A guide on how to start a rock collection and how to identify igneous, metamorphic, and sedimentary rocks. For ages four through eight.

Headstrom, Richard. *Suburban Geology.* Englewood Cliffs, NJ: Prentice-Hall, 1985.

> An introduction to common rocks and minerals.

Hiscock, Bruce. *The Big Rock.* New York: Atheneum, 1988.

> Traces the origin of a granite rock located near the Adirondack Mountains and describes how it reveals information about the history of the earth.

Lauber, Patricia. *Volcano.* New York: Bradbury Press, 1986.

> An account of how and why Mount St. Helens erupted in 1980, the destruction it caused, and the return of life to that area.

_____. *Dinosaurs Walked Here.* New York: Bradbury Press, 1987.

> Discusses how fossilized remains of plants and animals reveal the characteristics of the prehistoric world.

Martin, Alice Fitch, and Bertha Morris Parker. *Rocks and Minerals.* Racine, WI: Golden Press, 1974.

> An overview of rocks and minerals. Describes how they are formed and how they are used.

Murrow, Liza Ketchum. *Susan Humphris, Geologist.* Brattleboro, VT: Teacher's Laboratory, 1989.

> A biography of a marine geologist, discussing her childhood, schooling and training, daily work schedule, and the obstacles and challenges she faces as a woman scientist.

Selsam, Millicent E., and Joyce Hunt. *A First Look at Rocks.* New York: Walker and Company, 1984.

> Describes the distinguishing properties of various kinds of rocks.

Sipiera, Paul P. *I Can Be a Geologist.* Chicago: Children's Press, 1986.

> Briefly describes a variety of jobs and topics of study in the field of geology. Highlights the necessary education and training.

Symes, R. F., and R. R. Harding. *Crystal & Gem.* New York: Knopf, 1991.

> Describes the basic shapes of crystals and how they form in nature, how crystals are studied and identified, how crystals are grown artificially, and other aspects of crystallography.

Thomas, Margaret. *Volcano!* New York: Macmillan Children's Book Group, 1991.

> Examines the nature, origins, and dangers of volcanoes. Discusses the warning system that detects threatening eruptions.

Glossary

Alike: Acting or looking the same.

Brainstorm: To share ideas on a topic. People often brainstorm to solve a problem.

Cleavage: The process by which a mineral splits along a definite line.

Communicate: To share information and ideas through speaking, writing, or drawing.

Compare: To look at two or more things to see how they are alike or different.

Compass: A device used to tell direction by means of a magnetic needle.

Conglomerate: A type of rock formed from rounded pieces of other rock.

Crust: The hard, outside layer of the earth.

Crystal: A solid substance that has a definite shape or pattern.

Data: Information, such as that gathered during an experiment.

Describe: To use words to explain how something looks, feels, or acts.

Different: Not the same.

Dull: Not bright or shiny; not able to reflect light.

Experiment: A procedure that is carried out to investigate a scientific question.

Fair test: A test that compares two or more things by keeping everything the same except the thing being compared. A race is a fair test. Everyone starts at the same place and at the same time and ends at the same place. The only thing that is different is the speed of the runners.

Field test: A scientific test that is done in the area where the materials are found rather than in the laboratory. Rocks and minerals can be studied in the field.

Formation: A pattern or shape.

Fossil: Remains or traces of an organism that lived long ago that are preserved in the earth.

Fracture: The absence of cleavage.

Gem: A precious stone that has been cut and polished. Rubies and diamonds are gems.

Geologist: A scientist who studies rocks and minerals to learn more about the history of our earth.

Glassy: Shiny and smooth.

Graph: A diagram used to show the relationship between things.

Guess: To give an idea about something when you are not sure.

Hard: Firm, not soft.

Hardness: A property of a mineral. Hardness is tested by scratching a mineral sample with different objects. The harder a mineral, the more difficult it is to scratch.

Identifying color: The color of a mineral in powder form. Determined by performing a streak test.

Igneous: A type of rock that forms when melted rock cools.

Impurity: Something that mixes with another substance and usually reduces its quality.

Investigate: To study something closely and in an organized way.

Lava: Melted rock that erupts out of a volcano.

Length: The distance from one end of something to the other.

Lodestone: A form of the mineral magnetite; contains iron and acts as a magnet.

Luster: A property of a mineral. Luster is described by how the mineral reflects light.

Magma: Melted rock that is underground.

Magnetism: The ability of a substance to attract iron.

Measure: To find out the length, size, or weight of something.

Metamorphic: A type of rock that has been changed as a result of underground heat, pressure, and water.

Mineral: A solid substance found in nature that has distinctive properties, such as a crystal form.

Mohs scale: A system used to determine the relative hardness of minerals.

Observe: To use your senses to study something closely.

Opaque: Not able to let light pass through.

Pattern: A repeating arrangement of shapes, colors, numbers, or other things.

Pebble: A small, round stone.

Physical property: A characteristic of an object that can studied through the senses.

Plot: To locate a point or points on a graph.

Predict: To say what you think is going to happen.

Procedure: A set of steps that tells how to do something.

Property: Something about an object that helps tell what it is.

Rock: Material found in nature that may be made up of one or more minerals; clay, sand, and other earth materials; and fossils.

Rock cycle: The process by which rocks change to form new rocks. The changes in rocks are caused by many things, including heat, rain and snow, and underground pressure.

Same: Alike, not different.

Scratch: To cut or scrape.

Sediment: Pieces of rocks, minerals, and organic materials that are carried by water, wind, or ice.

Sedimentary: A type of rock that is formed from sediments that are carried by wind or water, dropped, and cemented or packed together.

Senses: Touch, taste, smell, sight, and hearing.

Shape: The form of an object.

Size: A measurement of how big something is.

Soft: Not hard or firm.

Sort: To put things together on the basis of a property, such as color or size.

Streak test: A test used to determine the identifying color of a mineral.

Surface: The outside or the top of an object.

Tool: An object used to do a task.

Translucent: Able to let some light pass through.

Transparent: Clear; able to let light through.

Unit: A fixed quantity used as a standard of measure. Inches, miles, meters, degrees, and kilograms are all units.

Volcano: An opening in the earth's crust through which lava, gases, and other materials can flow.

Waxy: Looking like wax; dull.

Weather: To age and break down as a result of the effects of wind, rain, and ice.

Weight: A measurement of how heavy something is.